DATA PULSE

A BRIEF TOUR OF ARTIFICIAL INTELLIGENCE IN HEALTHCARE

MATTHEW MARCETICH

New Degree Press

DATA PULSE

A Brief Tour of Artificial Intelligence in Healthcare

ISBN   978-1-64137-538-2   *Paperback*

978-1-64137-539-9   *Kindle Ebook*

978-1-64137-540-5   *Digital Ebook*

DEDICATION

———

Dedicated to my parents, Michael and Nada. To my brother, Adam, for his support and for his shared appreciation of art and science.

A special thank you to my mentors and advisers, whose talents and experiences far exceed their credentials, and for their quick responses to occasional late-night and weekend emails. Through their example and efforts, these individuals provide inspiration and encouragement to create a better future. These individuals include: Jim Potter, Mark Cochran, Mark Donowitz, Michelle Mynlieff, Kris Tym, John FP Bridges, Ed Bunker, and Karen Davis.

CONTENTS

ACKNOWLEDGMENTS

This is my first book and is far from perfect. It's a relatively short book that covers a lot of ground in a rapidly evolving field. I hope you will enjoy reading this book and will learn something new. Note: the book cover features open-source code (see Appendix) from BenevolentAI, a group that develops machine learning for drug discovery.

Thank you to my early supporters, who preordered a copy of the book or contributed to the crowd funding effort that supported the pre-publishing of this book, and to my interviewees—I hope this book shares a slice of their deep knowledge. A special thanks to Paniz Rezaeerod for her support, and for her help formatting references.

Thank you to the team at New Degree Press, especially Eric Koester who developed the Creator Institute at Georgetown University, Brian Bies, my cover designer Gjorgji Pejkovski, and my editors, Robert Keiser and Ryan Porter. Many thanks to the entire team including Ruslan Nabiev and Leila Summers who helped pull this all together. Writing this book was a neat experience, and the support and structure from the book-writing program pushed me to write this book in a relatively short period of time.

It is with gratitude that I acknowledge the following individuals who have been a part of the journey:

Anju Bhargava, PhD
Usama Bilal, MD, PhD, MPH
Ivana Brajkovic, MD
Mark Cochran, PhD
Kevin Daley, MS
Justin Dowsett
Hans Eguia, MD
Ryan Frank, MBA
Robert Frost
Daniel Martinez Garcia, MD, MPH
Ashley Flannery, MD
Emily Gerry, JD
Chris Hanna
Ahmed Hassoon, MD, MPH
Sloan Hatfield, JD
Leonard Hwostow, MBA
Jessica Jeang, MSF
Fabrice Jotterand, PhD, MA
Peter Kazanzides, PhD
Jamie Marcetich Keen
Mark King, JD
Eric Koester, JD
Jackie Kolosky, DO
Bob Lange
Maria Leasca
Kat Lee MBA, MA
Ting Lew
Jim Liew, PhD
Emily Little, MPH

Kamal Maheshwari, MD, MPH
Himanshu Makharia, MS
Adam Marcetich, MS
Michael and Nada Marcetich
Donna Marinkovich
Dushan Marinkovich
Melanie Markovina Mires
Strahinja Matejic, MA
Dejan Micic, MD
Branko Mikasinovich, PhD
Mina Miljevic, JD
Brian Naughton
Alexandra Novakovic, PhD
Dr. Don and Sally Novakovic
Natalie Olivo
Warren Pierson
Jim Potter
Brian Pyevich, MS
Paniz Rezaeerod
Elise Jeffress Ryan
Jason Sauve
Matt Grobis Sosna, PhD
Dan Takacs
Milica Tasic, MBA
Quoc Tran, MD
Stevan Verzich
Ryan Yurk
Phaedra Zeider Toral

PART 1: INTRODUCTION TO THE BASICS

CHAPTER 0:

INTRODUCTION

The speed with which health IT achieves its full potential depends far less on the technology than on whether its key stakeholders—government officials, technology vendors and innovators, health care administrators, physicians, training leaders, and patients—work together and make wise choices.

—ROBERT WACHTER, PHYSICIAN AND AUTHOR OF *THE DIGITAL DOCTOR*[1]

In the United States, nearly anyone who interacts with the health care system generates data. Your health data are generated in hospital administrative systems as soon as you check in for your appointment. Your data are generated and stored in electronic health record (EHR) systems, which began as billing systems and have grown to include lab data and research data. Health data are stored in population health records and used by state health departments to understand health trends and monitor disease spread. Even finance databases contain health data. After all, your spending habits

---

1   Robert Wachter, *The Digital Doctor: Hope, Hype, and Harm at the Dawn of Medicine's Computer Age*, McGraw-Hill Publishing, 2015.

can tell a story, albeit a partial one, of factors that could be affecting your health.

EHR data represent traditional health data: use and sharing of the data are regulated and protected, the data are derived directly from patient-physician encounters, and the data represent a combination of clinical details, behavioral patterns, research, and prescription drug and billing information. These data are generated during routine clinical care and emergency visits; the data are protected by the Health Insurance Portability and Accountability Act (HIPAA), which outlines a set of national standards for the protection of certain health information. Increasingly, health data are generated in nontraditional ways, in situations outside of physician-patient interactions. An employee wellness application collects health data, and thousands of health apps are available to collect nutrition and fitness data, to monitor blood sugar for diabetic children from afar, or to guide mothers through breastfeeding, as a few examples. If you have a smartphone, chances are your device is monitoring your heart rate or the number of steps you walked today.

Whether the data are traditional or nontraditional, widespread agreement among physicians and patients, and a bit of common sense and intuition, suggests that health data are highly personal. Traditional health data are also highly confidential while the confidentiality of nontraditional data is blurry, since the nontraditional health data are not legally protected. Depending on privacy agreements, the nontraditional health data could be sold or shared with third parties.

Especially for traditional health data, much effort is focused on keeping the data secure and confidential. Data are stored on encrypted databases, transmission of those data are monitored and encrypted (at rest and in transit), and the personal devices used to access health data (i.e., cell phones, computers) are ideally—but not always—designated for the sole purpose of handling health data. Some medical institutions take extra precautions by evaluating the data integrity risks of any device that touches health data and requiring those devices to be monitored.

Such protections lead to administrative burdens and ethical dilemmas. The incoming medical student wonders: *Should I set up email forwarding from my hospital email account to my personal email for convenience?* The clinical data scientist, who is checking their email on a Friday afternoon from a local coffee shop, wonders: *Is it okay to use the public Wi-Fi on my work computer, even if I'm not emailing any health data?* Under data trust policies governing traditional health data, casual access to and sharing of health data are forbidden, and academic medical centers are increasingly providing analytical tools that reside behind institutional firewalls to allow staff and students to develop analytical tools in protected virtual environments. Use of virtual private networks (VPNs) are becoming mandatory when connecting to public Wi-Fi networks; at some institutions, the VPN will evaluate a foreign Wi-Fi network for potential vulnerabilities before establishing a connection.

In the United States, nurses, medical doctors, and pharmacists are ranked as the most trusted occupations.[2] They earn trust by relating and listening to the patient, by adhering to privacy

---

2   Niall McCarthy, "America's Most and Least Trusted Professions," Forbes, accessed on March 31, 2020.

and ethical standards, and through an inherent responsibility to help the patient through medical circumstances ranging from benign to catastrophic. As use and governance of health data permeate the continuum of health care delivery, the role of technical occupations, such as computer engineers and data scientists, will become increasingly important. And while these professions are not outlined in the list of most trusted occupations, probably because of their hidden role in health care, perhaps one day they will be included.

During the course of medical care, data are generated in a multitude of ways. Let's take a look at a few possible scenarios:

- Scenario 1: The patient walks into the pharmacy with a sore throat, approaches the pharmacist, who is helping another patient while placing a physician on hold, and describes her symptoms. The pharmacist finishes his phone call and then takes a throat swab of the patient and performs a test for Group A streptococcus bacteria. He gets results within minutes. Laws in some states, including Ohio, are changing to allow pharmacists to perform or order clinical tests.[3] If the test is negative, the pharmacist reassures and directs the patient to aisle seven for over-the-counter cold medication, cautioning that the patient should see a physician if the symptoms persist, and especially if she begins to develop a fever. If the test is positive, the pharmacist advises the patient to see a nurse practitioner or physician right away for appropriate treatment.

3   "Soon you could visit your pharmacist instead of your primary care doctor for common ailments," News 5 Cleveland, January 15, 2019.

- Scenario 2: During a scheduled yearly physical exam, the physician introduces herself to the patient as she sits down across from the patient while logging into her clinic's desktop computer. She mentions that the clinic uses an EHR system to record data from patient visits, which allows the patient to set up an account to schedule another visit, view lab results, and check their prescriptions. During the course of the physical exam, the physician receives an electronic reminder to screen for hepatitis C based on CDC recommendations. The patient decides to enroll to receive electronic notifications from the EHR system. In a few moments, the patient receives an email with a link to the system's secure portal. The next day, the patient receives a phone call from his physician, who notifies him that he tested positive for hepatitis C, a serious but treatable condition. During the phone call, the physician outlines a course of treatment and mentions that treatment details will be provided in the EHR system. (Note: if possible, the physician will ask to see the patient in person to discuss treatment options although telemedicine is increasingly used to facilitate virtual consultations.) After logging in to the EHR, the patient sees his test results and a reassuring note from his physician. Given the patient's insurance and the lab results, his physician suggests a regimen of glecaprevir for eight weeks followed by sofosbuvir for twelve weeks. The physician scheduled follow-up visits and lab work, which are viewable in a calendar in the patient's health record portal.
- Scenario 3: The patient, with a routine history of inflammatory bowel disease, logs in to her personal health account to review her doctor's instructions for her

upcoming colonoscopy. The patient receives reminders multiple days in advance of the appointment that describe how to prepare for the colonoscopy. She follows instructions outlined in the reminders. After checking in to the clinic for the colonoscopy, the doctor asks the patient if she prepared for the procedure and checks a box on the patient's electronic file indicating that the patient has prepared. This detail is relevant, since the patient had decided three years ago to enroll in a research study interested in the genetics of inflammatory bowel disease (IBD). During the procedure, a few colonic biopsies are collected by the physician and picked up by a member of the research team performing the study. As part of the procedure, the physician takes photos of the patient's intestinal tract—photos of normal and inflamed tissue—which are included in the patient's electronic file. The physician notes the biopsy locations within the colon. Prior to the visit, the patient signed a consent form agreeing to use biopsy samples for IBD research. Given the patient's willingness to participate in research, the physician was able to compare her images with prior stored images to identify an improvement in disease activity, demonstrating that her therapy is working.

- Scenario 4: The patient decides to enroll in her company's health rewards program, which offers a Fitbit wearable device. Competitive by nature and a former collegiate marathon runner, she decides she wants to win the program's grand prize. She modifies her commute so she can walk to work every day, works out five times per week, and allows the health program to access her personal health data recorded through the Fitbit.

In all of the scenarios described above, health data are generated. In scenarios (2, 3, and 4) where the data are recorded, they are recorded electronically. In Scenario 3, the patient knowingly contributes to an ongoing research study. Only in Scenarios 2 and 3 are the patient's health data protected by HIPAA, which outlines a set of national standards for the protection of certain health information. HIPAA was first introduced in 1996, well before the emergence of EHRs, with the idea that most health data would be contained within a traditional health record. Since its introduction, HIPAA has undergone numerous amendments to safeguard unauthorized use and sharing of health data, which have largely transitioned from paper to electronic forms.

The health data in Scenario 4 are recorded electronically, but their protection under HIPAA falls into a legal gray area. If the wellness program is structured into the employer's health plan, the patient data collected into the program are protected by HIPAA.[4] Health data collected by health devices, diet programs, experiments in mindfulness, sleep tracking, and even physical therapy massages at your local gym are recorded electronically and provide a larger picture into the overall health of the patient—but they may or may not fall under the umbrella of HIPAA protection.

The scenarios above are just a few of the many examples that form the foundation for artificial intelligence (AI) tools developed to understand patterns in disease progression. AI

---

4   "HIPAA Privacy and Security and Workplace Wellness Programs," US Department of Health and Human Services, accessed on March 30, 2020.

tools make sense of data patterns, which can begin at the individual level. To provide any meaningful output, however, AI tools need to be trained on and developed with a large amount of data. Enterprise health AI tools can depend on the aggregated data for millions of patients. The more diverse the data, the better—not simply for statistical power, but also to assuage hidden biases.

Companies that develop health AI tools require access to personal health data, even if they are not the health provider. HIPAA rules define whether the personal health data need to be de-identified. Sometimes, companies develop their own tools and platforms to collect health data and generate low-cost results for the customer. One example, 23andMe, collects data by selling an inexpensive genetic profiling service. The customer pays 23andMe to perform genetic sequencing on a saliva sample. In return, 23andMe sends the customer an easy-to-understand sequencing report on a portion of their genome. As more and more customers request genetic testing, 23andMe collects genetic data from individuals that can tell broader public health stories when analyzed in aggregate. When combined with clinical data, companies begin to make associations between genetic results and clinical outcomes—a powerful combination.

A company such as 23andMe can acquire clinical data in a variety of ways. One strategy is to partner with academic medical centers. Another strategy is to merge with another company that has already collected clinical data. In November 2019, Google joined forces with a large health care provider, Ascension, which operates 150 hospitals and more than fifty senior living facilities across the United States.[5] The health care data and cloud computing deal could result in the development of AI tools built on the foundation of historical health data collected and maintained by Ascension, as Ascension aims to use AI to help improve clinical effectiveness and patient safety.[6] Such partnerships are subject to data use agreements and to business associate agreements (BAAs), which define how clinical, HIPAA-protected data can be safely used and disclosed to third parties.[7]

Health care providers are stewards of vast amounts of historical health data, and Google's recent deal with Ascension is just one of many examples of commercial partnerships. Agreements such as the one between Google and Ascension could potentially lead to meaningful predictive tools based on years of historical data on thousands to millions of patients.

Could patients whose care was overseen by Ascension have predicted their data would be used for potential development of AI tools? Could Ascension have supported its own internal resources to develop AI tools, or does it just make sense for health providers to partner with large tech firms that have the expertise and resources needed to develop AI tools? Academic and industry partnerships in health care are becoming a trend, and the Google-Ascension deal is just one example.

---

5   Dave Paresh, "Google signs healthcare data and cloud computing deal with Ascension," Reuters, November 11, 2019.

6   Ibid.

7   "Business Associate Contracts," US Department of Health and Human Services, accessed on March 31, 2020.

As consumers of health care and as constant generators of personal health data, individuals need to understand how machine learning (ML) tools are developed and implemented within health care, as they involve important implications for personal privacy. Development of AI tools in health care could usher in a paradigm shift in the relationship between patients and providers as one that resembles more of a partnership. For individuals, the opportunities to contribute to health tools could have far-reaching impacts.

* * *

In 2013, about 153 exabytes of health care data were produced globally, and about 2,314 exabytes will be produced in 2020 (where one exabyte = 1 billion gigabytes).[8] Increasingly, health data are stored in the "cloud," rather than physically in the doctor's or hospital's office. Ultimately, the cloud is a computer managed by a company (like Google or Amazon) that hosts the equipment and provides access to the data stored on the device. Private clouds are also used in large academic medical centers to preserve compliance to HIPAA, and vendors of managed health information systems provide templates and configurations that enforce HIPAA compliance.

The real power of AI tools is revealed when analyzing massive amounts of data stored in the cloud. Artificial intelligence tools make sense of these vast quantities of data by identifying patterns that would take humans a lifetime to find.

---

8   "Harnessing the Power of Data in Health," Stanford Medicine 2017 University Trends Report, Stanford University, accessed on October 3, 2019.

Over the past five to ten years, AI tools have been implemented in health care settings to address administrative burdens and, to a lesser degree, clinical issues. In the United States, the administrative burden on health care is huge and contributes greatly to the high cost of health care when compared to other developed countries. In 2017, national health expenditures in the United States grew 3.9 percent to $3.5 trillion—about $10,739 per person—and accounted for 17.9 percent of GDP. The Centers for Medicare and Medicaid Services (CMS) estimate that national health spending is projected to grow at an average rate of 5.5 percent per year through 2027, reaching nearly $6 trillion by 2027. Despite its high cost, the US health care system as a whole is outperformed by other developed countries[9]; while AI is not a magic bullet, strategic uses of AI could improve care process and administrative efficiency. One group that we'll learn about later in the book, macro-eyes, is developing AI tools to predict when patients will show up for their scheduled appointments in an effort to help providers estimate clinical demand and staffing needs.

Given the high cost of health care, developing AI tools to address administrative challenges makes sense—such as scheduling appointments and predicting readmission rates. Clinical and research areas of health care are also ripe for applications of AI tools, even if the financial incentive is not so obvious. And while financial incentives are important, quality of care for the patient is paramount. As we will see, AI has already been implemented in drug discovery and

9   Eric Schneider, et al, "Mirror, Mirror 2017: International Comparison Reflects Flaws and Opportunities for Better US Health Care," The Commonwealth Fund, accessed on September 28, 2019.

development and is used to determine and expedite pathology diagnoses, among other uses that improve patient well-being.

While history has shown the enthusiasm for AI swelling and deflating, the current enthusiasm for development of AI tools is palpable. Support for development of AI tools for health care is evident in funding for startups in the space. According to a report by Rock Health, AI/ML-powered digital health companies raised over $2 billion in 2018—a massive 161 percent increase over 2017.[10] These numbers only account for investments in privately held companies.

The increase in AI/ML activity in research labs and large publicly held companies—like Google and Microsoft—also signals a trend toward experimentation with AI. To be sure, investment in early-stage companies comes with risk, and investments are not always profitable or sustainable. Large companies pursuing aggressive AI ideas are not immune to potential financial loss either. Alphabet's DeepMind is one example. DeepMind, the artificial intelligence subsidiary of Alphabet (Google's parent company) saw its losses rise by 55 percent to $571 million as its debts soared to more than $1.2 billion in 2019.[10]

UTILIZING AI IN THE HEALTH CARE MARKETPLACE

The underlying theory that drives health AI tools today was first developed decades ago. Early health care AI tools in the 1970s and '80s focused on clinical decision-making

---

10 Sean Day, "2018 Funding Part 2: Seven more takeaways from digital health's $8.1B year," Rock Health, accessed on October 2, 2019.

and pattern recognition. At the time, researchers knew that computer-driven tools could scan, store, and interpret vast amounts of health data much more quickly than any human ever could, even if the hardware was in its infancy and storage of health data in electronic form was a vision.

Today, in dark hospital corridors, storage rooms contain file cabinets with millions of microscope slides used to diagnose tissue pathology. These microscope slides are catalogued for retrieval at a later date and read by a pathologist who confirms and documents a diagnosis based on the morphology of the tissue. Thinking back to Scenario 3 described earlier, the pathologist confirms the diagnosis of low-grade dysplasia suspected by the physician performing the colonoscopy. Since the patient has a history of inflammatory bowel disease and has returned to the same clinic for her colonoscopy appointments, the pathology department has a historical record of her biopsies in the form of microscope slides. The microscope slides actually represent an early form of health data. The cabinets are the "servers" that store the slides. And, at a later date, these slides can be retrieved for research purposes, to confirm a diagnosis, or as part of a case study.

A scientist might request pathology slides for patients with a diagnosis of high-grade dysplasia and inspect those slides for patterns in the slide images. Historically, the process of selecting a microscope slide from a room of file cabinets, confirming the slide is correct, and then reading the slide with a microscope has been a manual one. Now, computational tools using AI are developed to understand patterns within the pathology images and to convert and interpret these slides as image files. Computer algorithms scan through millions of images to detect pathological patterns, and they do so without physical fatigue. In other words, a computer can tirelessly analyze millions of image files and discern patterns from those images while the human eye would become tired and fatigued after several hundred.

By accurately processing vast amounts of health data, informatics teams have created systems for detecting life-threatening diseases. Many of these systems are still relegated to research and are not approved for clinical use, but ultimately these tools will augment decision-making of human health care providers. In the case of pathology slides, computer algorithms are trained to understand patterns in cellular morphology to distinguish "normal" tissue from "pathologic" and various stages in between. Such advances give the physician more power to make an accurate and efficient diagnosis, decreasing the cost of health care and potentially saving lives if a diagnosis is caught faster.

Contents of an image file are read into a computer through an AI technique called computer vision. In areas where war or natural disasters destroy medical and demographic records, public health researchers use computer vision and other AI techniques to make a reasonable estimate of someone's age by training computer algorithms to understand facial images. In places like rural Senegal, infrastructure does not exist to maintain demographic records, yet community health workers are responsible for delivering care that relies on an accurate measure of someone's age.

As we will see, computer vision tools can help the community health worker in rural Senegal fill gaps in missing demographic information. The use of AI in health care extends from dark laboratories in hospital basements to sub-Saharan Africa—and many places in between.

ETHICAL DILEMMAS

Aside from the financial risks and barriers of implementing AI tools in health care, we have ethical challenges to overcome. What happens if an algorithm misses a life-altering diagnosis? Is the algorithm's error worse than that of a human physician?

By developing AI tools in health care, computer programs have the ability to make clinical decisions related to human diseases. Should the algorithm have its own agency and responsibility?

During employment training as new hires, we learn about implicit bias and how having unconscious biases based on our life experiences is normal. The danger for us is letting those biases we don't consciously recognize go unchecked. How much ethical elbowroom should we allow AI tools, and can we eliminate bias? Within AI, can we identify an analogous form of implicit bias and, if so, can we prevent these biases from adversely affecting a clinical outcome?

How do we know when a machine learning algorithm is accurate enough to influence human decision-making? We have already ceded some autonomy and much trust in the use of AI algorithms in other industries—sometimes unknowingly, like the spam filter on your email. In the case of the email spam filter, we accept the inaccuracy of a misclassified email as a minor nuisance. Consider the following example:

> For some reason I didn't receive the dinner invitation from Aunt Suzie that I was expecting yesterday by email. Why don't I call her to confirm? Sure enough, Aunt Suzie had sent the email yesterday, but the email was routed to the spam folder. To avoid missed emails from Aunt Suzie, I'll move that email into the inbox folder, so my email knows that messages from Aunt Suzie are not spam.

While the example above may seem like a simple rule engine (i.e., tell the computer algorithm that all emails from Aunt Suzie are not spam), a machine learning algorithm running in the background will look for details like content of the subject line, tone of message, any imbedded links, and salutation as clues to classify the message as not spam. But in health care, misclassification can be much more problematic, especially when influencing clinical decision-making.

DISCOVERING AI'S POTENTIAL

During my formative years at the Johns Hopkins University School of Medicine, I worked in an environment that encouraged learning about many health-related disciplines and their relationship to each other. While my observation sounds parochial now, it became clear to me that computers and health care could work together to create new bioinformatics tools that were predictive and diagnostic in nature. By attending classes and research lectures, and by supporting an open-source software application used for medical research, it became clear that public health tools developed in Baltimore have effects with global reach.

This environment was exactly what I needed early in my career—to be immersed in and enamored by medical advances at the intersection of new technology. I noted quite quickly how much I didn't know, how much more I needed to learn, and that the process of developing and applying health tools was mediated by often complex and intricate business arrangements.

Following my experiences at Johns Hopkins, I managed a team at an AI consulting company that develops custom machine learning software applications in the federal tech space. We developed analytic tools to better understand federal grants data and were recognized two years in a row by government innovation awards. Through this experience, I learned to deploy computer code to make a research idea available to millions of potential users.

Given my background, I'm interested in developing and supporting health care AI tools that will be available to a wide range of users and ultimately improve lives. These users represent the patient, the provider, and the payer (i.e., the insurance company). Ultimately, health care AI tools will be effective if they can respond to medical conditions but also prevent people from becoming patients in the first place.

* * *

My interests in health care began at a young age, as my father was a pharmacist at a locally owned pharmacy in suburban

Southeastern Wisconsin. Our family dinner table discussions would sometimes include reflections on my father's busy day in a retail pharmacy. My fascination for business and health care grew, and I found my father's dedication to customer service admirable. He went the extra mile to support his customers, sometimes missing dinner to help a patient who came to the pharmacy at closing time. Indeed, this is a shared experience for many health professionals who support patient care.

When I was a young child, our first family computer, an Apple IIe, was a gift from my godfather. We set up the computer in our dining room, next to the dining room table. I fondly recall many afternoons playing Number Munchers and hearing the literal "crunch" of the computer as it read the five-inch floppy disk. A fascination for science and math turned into passions, leading me to a desire to find ways to improve health care. After discovering data science and machine learning, I wanted to learn more about applications of AI in health care and the steps needed to develop the technology.

AUGMENTING HEALTH CARE, PARTICULARLY IN THE US

The intersection of AI and health care is not new, but increased sophistication and availability of technology have enabled accelerated progress in recent years. Given the continued interest and development of AI tools, the way you receive health care has already changed, even though you may not yet know it. The technologies brewing in academic medical centers, in Silicon Valley, and even in off-grid central Wisconsin, have wide-reaching effects that may improve health care in unsuspected ways. Yet these are accompanied by ethical and financial risks.

Funding for AI/ML in health care is robust, which will surely lead to the creation of new industries and also new challenges. President Donald Trump's FY 2021 budget "prioritizes the Industries of the Future and commits to double R&D spending in nondefense artificial intelligence (AI) and quantum information science (QIS) by 2022."[11] Will public policy and ethical decision-making keep up with the pace of change? So far, we've identified some risks in developing and implementing AI in health care settings, and while some benefits are clear, technologists and physicians have only planted the seeds of new concepts and breakthroughs.

With the aid of AI tools, diagnoses are quicker and, in some cases, more accurate. In cardiology, machine learning tools can automatically detect anomalies in electrocardiograms with an accuracy of 92 percent.[12] According to some epidemiology researchers, "Machine learning could be used to increase the speed and potentially the accuracy (provided high-quality input data) of identification of the source of ongoing outbreaks, leading to more efficient treatment and prevention of additional cases" of food-borne disease outbreaks.[13] Although we must point out some of the failed attempts too, such as the

---

11 "President Trump's FY 2021 Budget Commits to Double Investments in Key Industries of the Future," White House press release, February 11, 2020.

12 Renato Cuocolo, et al, "Current applications of big data and machine learning in cardiology." *Journal of Geriatric Cardiology* 16, no. 8 (2019): 601.

13 Baiba Vilne, et al, "Machine Learning Approaches for Epidemiological Investigations of Food-Borne Disease Outbreaks." *Frontiers in Microbiology* 10, (2019).

failure of Google Flu Trends to predict the peak of flu season in 2013, we have seen far more positive outcomes.[14] Consider this example: according to current research in Senegal from Dr. Stephane Helleringer of the Johns Hopkins Bloomberg School of Public Health, facial recognition using computer vision is being piloted in rural settings where birth records are scarce or damaged, thereby allowing health researchers to deliver more accurate care and track disease more effectively.

THE AUTHOR'S TAKE

I think a fundamental understanding of how machine learning affects health care is important for any patient, since personal data are being used for predictive health tools and the technology is here to stay. As patients, we can use this knowledge to better understand the health care we receive and hold better informed conversations with our providers. We can probably also have better informed conversations with fellow patients and perhaps find new ways to contribute in positive ways to our health care and the health care of others. And, from the standpoint of providers, understanding the role of machine learning in their determination of diagnoses can strengthen their resolve in decision-making, show them the pitfalls of a computer-aided diagnosis, and maybe even identify some scenarios when it's better not to use machine learning.

Within health care, AI touches administration, research, and clinical settings. This book is a humble attempt to provide a snapshot of the current state of AI in health care, including

---

14   David Lazer, "What We Can Learn from the Epic Failure of Google Flu Trends," *Wired*, accessed on October 1, 2015.

essential legal and ethical challenges, from a mostly US perspective.

Throughout the book, I give credit to other authors in the field, and I hope the Appendix serves as a good resource for anyone who wants to dive deeper. I should probably point out that several books can be (and have been) written on each chapter alone, so this book is by no means a comprehensive account—each chapter can be studied in much greater detail, so for someone new to the field, I hope it's a good place to start. To be sure, this book stands on the shoulders of decades of previous work in the field, which is likely an indication that we have decades of progress ahead. As someone who has been a receiver of health care, and as someone with technical and research exposure to machine learning and medical research, I hope my perspective will enlighten you as a reader in an approachable way.

AI TECHNOLOGY: WHERE ARE WE GOING?

In a world where computers can identify diseases more quickly and sometimes more accurately than humans, we should take next steps to better understand how to implement the technology. It's still unlikely that researchers will replace your general physician with a modern C-3PO, but systems that will augment and improve the decision-making of your primary care physician, pharmacist, nurse practitioner, or physician assistant are well underway. We hold as common knowledge that health providers are overburdened, in large part by administrative tasks—some of which can be reliably performed by carefully developed AI tools. Administrivia aside, clinical processes and development of prescription medications can be augmented by AI algorithms, leading to quicker and more accurate diagnoses and shorter development time.

This book is for early adopters of machine learning and AI tools in support of health care. It's also intended for anyone who wants to engage with the topic and has read some interesting headlines about breakthroughs in the field. If you are a student, my hope is that this book will give you some new resources and potential ideas to pursue. If you are a patient, I hope this book will give you a fundamental understanding of how health care AI tools work, so you can have better informed conversations with your doctor, and so you will have a better understanding of how your health care could be used to develop AI tools to help large populations of patients. And at the end of the day, I think we're all students and patients.

Parts of this book and some of the examples might serve as a historical record of progress in the field. Will our risk tolerance for adoption of health care AI loosen, and do we have a good understanding of the risks? New possibilities will emerge, new benefits will surface, and some existing tools will be rendered obsolete. The fabric of health care delivery will change, but human caregivers will still be at the epicenter of decision-making, in a human-AI partnership that wrestles with constantly evolving ethical conundrums.

With change, we will always see tension—particularly if decision-making is replaced or augmented. Some human stakeholders—physicians, nurses, administrators—will worry about job replacement. Some patients will wonder if they can really trust the computer-generated text response they receive when texting their virtual nurse. The medicinal chemist will review the list of candidate drug structures generated by open-source machine learning programs, knowing the algorithms producing those structures were developed collaboratively by skilled and well-intentioned computer programmers. While this book is written with a US focus, we need to determine whether our fears of more widespread implementation of AI are warranted or are holding us back from revolutionizing global health care delivery.

CHAPTER 1:

A HISTORY OF AI

In the last decade, AI went from niche to mainstream.
I wonder what our community will accomplish
this decade?

—ANDREW NG, COFOUNDER OF COURSERA AND AI EXPERT[15]

DR. ROBERT MILLER

My introduction to artificial intelligence stemmed from a curiosity of applying machine learning to health care data while working at the Johns Hopkins University School of Medicine. I was inspired by precision medicine efforts at Johns Hopkins and other institutions, so I spent my spare time during evenings and weekends learning basic programming skills related to machine learning. I was humbled by the depth of experience of some of the professors I met along the way, and I am grateful for being able to interview some of them.

Dr. Robert Miller, a seasoned pathologist at Johns Hopkins, with whom I had the pleasure of working on a biobanking project, illuminated the historical depth of AI by using entertaining anecdotes told as only a passionate and jovial

---

15   Andrew Ng. Twitter Post. January 1, 2020, 3:23 AM.

physician could. During our conversations, sometimes over coffee in the Daily Grind coffee shop on campus, he shared his seemingly encyclopedic knowledge of health IT.

* * *

In one conversation, Dr. Miller acknowledged the continuing uncertainty about the direction the medical field is taking with applications of artificial intelligence. Decades ago, few could have predicted how AI applications in health care would give rise to current ethical and legal dilemmas, to say nothing of the potential threats to the jobs of at least some health care professionals—although clues may have been apparent even in the earliest days of AI. But despite ongoing uncertainties, the field will continue moving forward—even if the process is not always smooth and mistakes continue to be made. When thinking of the possible shortcomings of AI applied to health care, Dr. Miller is reminded of Henry Petroski, an engineer and historian who studies engineering failures.

A particular example that Petroski describes[16] is a study of the structural failures of bridges by Paul Sibly,[17] who found that catastrophic failures of bridges in the United Kingdom and in North America occurred approximately every thirty years from the middle of the nineteenth century through about 1970. Although attributing these failures simply to successive "professional generations" of engineers and bridge

---

16   Henry Petroski, "Patterns of Failure," Modern Steel Construction, July 2006.

17   Paul Sibly, "The Production of Structural Failures," PhD Thesis, University of London, 1977.

builders may be tempting, Sibley found that in each instance, the structural failures of the bridges could be predicted from the unsafe extrapolations of existing bridge designs and/or construction procedures that arose from the desire for taller, longer, and/or more massive bridge structures. To be clear, Petroski's bridge failures don't really apply to AI, but safety implications should be considered as in any engineering discipline. Despite the increasing use of machine learning in high-stakes and safety-critical applications such as health care, the field fundamentally lacks a framework for reasoning about failures and their potentially catastrophic effects.[18] More established fields of engineering, such as bridge design, have now developed such frameworks.

Dr. Miller makes the point that the field of AI and its applications to health care are still very young, even though they have built on decades of research in the field. At the current pace of AI development in health care, we need to be cautious as we become more dependent on AI tools for diagnosis, treatment, and other high-risk decisions in health care.

Unlike the more mature and established fields of architecture or structural engineering, the history of AI does not extend far enough back in time to provide similar lessons to those Petroski describes. In health care AI, we haven't seen any grand failures affecting patient care analogous to a bridge collapse. Since applied AI has a short history, Dr. Miller suggests that we still don't fully understand where AI

18 Suchi Saria and Adarsh Subbaswamy, "Tutorial: Safe and Reliable Machine Learning." In ACM Conference on Fairness, Accountability, and Transparency, 2019.

fits within health care, and that the current uses of machine learning in health care should be considered as "*imperfect classifiers* with *nondeterministic algorithms* with a tendency *for spurious errors.*" In other words, Dr. Miller is cautiously optimistic about AI's uses in medicine but acknowledges that we still have a lot to learn about the underlying technologies.

In another conversation, Dr. Miller recalls attending a NIH conference over forty years ago that featured a relatively new technology: the CT scanner, which became the basis of the explosive growth in digital radiology and tomography over the ensuing decades, with cumulative worldwide expenditures in the trillions of dollars for development and use of CT, MRI, PET, PET-CT, and related "digital radiology" modalities.

Many projected the multitrillion-dollar expenditures of the ensuing decades for this new technology, although adoption of computed tomography (CT) was slow as the technology wasn't initially viewed as affordable, even though it had clear technical and operational benefits. Despite the slow uptake, the importance of CT technology was widely recognized. In 1979, the Nobel Prize in Physiology or Medicine was awarded jointly to Allan Cormack and Godfrey Hounsfield for the development of computed tomography. Today, CT scans augment x-ray and ultrasound imaging and aid in detecting tumors, bone fractures, and other tissue anomalies that can be diagnosed based on changes in tissue density and morphology. Similar to CT scans, AI tools created today may not meet all three conditions of feasibility: *technical, economic,* and *operational,* but in the future, AI technologies may also fundamentally change how medical diagnoses and clinical decisions are made.

While Dr. Miller's primary focus is not AI, his path to medicine is somewhat emblematic of some of the pathways to learning and implementing AI tools in health care today. As a physics major in college, Dr. Miller had not originally planned to go to medical school, but after attending medical school and completing training in internal medicine and pathology, he became interested in computers in the late 1960s through evening courses and conversations with colleagues and others. Dr. Miller describes, "There was no internet back then, and Unix and minicomputers were just emerging as an alternative to expensive mainframes." At that time, he programmed in BASIC: Beginner's All-purpose Symbolic Instruction Code. Later, he relied on dial-up connections to communicate with his colleagues at Hopkins and elsewhere. Today, Unix forms the basis of Apple's macOS operating system; it helped spawn the minicomputer revolution, which preceded the explosive growth of the microcomputer or "personal computer." With his expertise in pathology and evolving knowledge in computers and informatics, Dr. Miller spent much of his career at Johns Hopkins developing laboratory and clinical information systems. He now enjoys teaching students about clinical informatics, including how emerging AI tools may impact electronic health record (EHR) systems and the management of patients' illnesses and health.

The 1960s had at least a few applications of AI to health care. Health data were not "structured" as we know it today. Structured data (and related data standards) help machines read data in both a reliable and repeatable manner. Paper and pen dominated as the tools for documenting clinical records. Fax machines emerged as the "modern" method of communicating and sharing clinical results. And even if clinical data of the time were structured, computational power could not support the programming tools needed to reliably read and process the data. Today, some hospitals still require the use of fax to transfer medical records, yet many millennials (or younger generations) who are reading this book may have never actually used a fax machine. (Will we still use fax machines ten years from now?) The chapters that follow highlight some ways AI can reduce administrative burdens.

According to Dr. Miller and many others, AI has developed leaps and bounds from where it began almost seventy years ago. While only recently have we seen a proliferation of health care-specific examples, the 1950s and '60s were a period of significant growth for AI.

HUMBLE BEGINNINGS

The origins of the field of AI begin somewhere around the early 1940s with the McCulloch-Pitts (MCP) neuron in 1943. Neuroscientist Warren McCulloch and logician Walter Pitts were interested in understanding how the neurons in the brain functioned and described the neuron as a nerve cell behaving as a simple logical gate with a binary output. Multiple signals would arrive at the dendrites and be aggregated up into the cell body. If the signal reached over a given threshold, it would fire and the signal would be transmitted across the axon to the next set of nerve cells. This biological process inspired computer scientists to develop neural networks. The basic structure of a neural network, the perceptron, is inspired by the neuron.

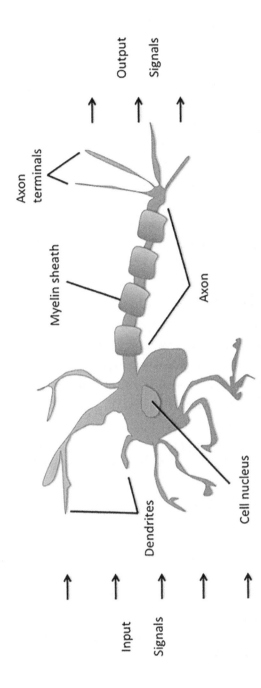

Figure 1.1: An example neuron[19], which would serve as the inspiration for the perceptron—the building block of neural networks.

19 Sebastian Raschka. Single-Layer Neural Networks and Gradient Descent, accessed April 27, 2020.

The term AI was first coined in the 1950s at a workshop held in 1956 at Dartmouth College and organized by computer scientist John McCarty, who later became a professor at Stanford.[20] McCarty is also credited for founding the Lisp computer language—a language that nowadays is considered obscure but still useful and is behind at least one self-made billionaire currently in his early thirties.[21]

At the start of the decade, English computer scientist and mathematician Alan Turing invented the Turing Test—a cognitive test determining if computer behavior was indistinguishable from human behavior. Turing had worked as a cryptographer in England during World War II, and in the late 1930s, he famously contributed to statistical models that helped decrypt messages exchanged by the German naval enigma. Also in the 1950s, computer scientist Arthur Lee Samuel began to teach computers how to play checkers[22] and is credited for being one of the early contributors to the fields of AI and machine learning. Between the Turing Test and examples of semi-autonomous computer programs like the one developed by Samuel, the idea of comparing computer intelligence to human intelligence began to develop.

In the late 1950s, the initial building block of neural networks—the perceptron—emerged through the work of

20　Kathleen Walch, "Artificial Intelligence Is Not a Technology," *Forbes*, accessed on August 10, 2019.

21　Derek Anderson, "The story behind payment disruptor stripe.com and its founder Patrick Collison." Tech Crunch, accessed on July 20, 2019.

22　Arthur L. Samuel, "Some Studies in Machine Learning Using the Game of Checkers," IBM Journal of Research and Development, 44: 206–226.

psychologist and neurobiologist Frank Rosenblatt. In 1957, Rosenblatt built upon the MCP neuron and constructed the first perceptron that could learn from data. Perceptrons are the single units of decision-making that comprise neural networks—a collection of algorithms designed to make decisions as if a network of neurons were firing. Learning occurred as the weights changed to fit the output, and the weights could be updated using a simple loop and mathematical equation or updating rule. Large neural networks can contain millions of perceptrons and require significant computational power when analyzing large datasets—the computational power that did not exist (and was prohibitively expensive) at that time. The perceptron provided a great first step forward and worked well for datasets that could be linearly separated. Figure 1.2 below shows the basics of a perceptron algorithm, which receives inputs and calculates an output after running those inputs through functions and optimized weights.

Artificial intelligence was concerned with solving formal math tasks, finding patterns in numbers, and dealing with pure mathematics. Applications of artificial intelligence expanded out of the traditional arenas of computer science to psychology, neurobiology, and studying human behavior. Today, artificial intelligence is popularized by notions of autonomous robots and, in medicine, surgical robotics (which are not always accurate representations of AI) and telemedicine. News headlines today sometimes highlight predictive diagnostic tests although their complexity and the cost of development and implementation are in early stages of understanding.

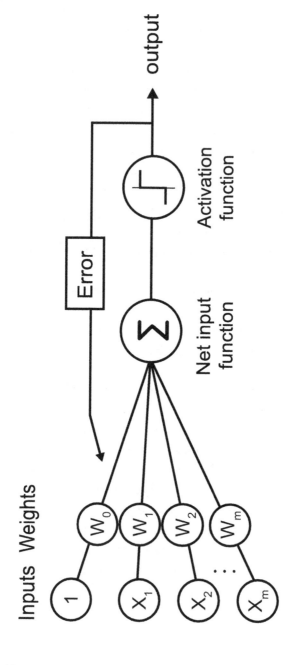

Figure 1.2: A representation of a perceptron[23], loosely based on the structure of a neuron.

23 Sebastian Raschka. Single-Layer Neural Networks and Gradient Descent, accessed April 27, 2020.

Into the 1960s and '70s, interest in the field of AI began to grow. As the complexity of tasks carried out by AI increased, computer scientists, neurobiologists, and psychologists began to imagine computers having cognitive ability and making decisions in a similar way to humans. Philosophers conjured thoughts of computers having humanlike intelligence. While the thoughts and goals of the scientific and philosophical communities were founded on good intentions, some viewed the emerging technologies as competitive and potentially adversarial. Dr. Miller recalls the AI Winter of the 1970s and later a collaboration between industry and government called the Fifth Generation Project, more formally known as Fifth Generation Computer Systems (FGCS). This project was started in 1982 by Japan's Ministry of International Trade and Industry (MITI) and built on the concept of knowledge representation. It sought to create computer systems that could represent facts and rules as formal logic propositions and then later operate on these facts for problem-solving. Around that time in the 1980s, US psychologist David Rumelhart rediscovered the famous backpropagation algorithm, which is now considered to be at the core of the current "AI revolution."[24] This algorithm, which is central to today's applications of neural networks, first arose in the field of control theory in the 1950s and '60s. One of its early applications was to optimize the thrusts of the Apollo spaceships as they headed toward the moon.[25]

Some predicted FGCS would take over the world with AI, which prompted fear and worry. In the early 1980s, medical

---

24   Michael I. Jordan, "Artificial Intelligence—The revolution hasn't happened yet," Amazon Science, accessed on November 25, 2019.

25   Ibid.

AI projects were responsible in part for the explosion of public interest in these so-called expert systems.[26] In other industries, and in a lesser limelight compared to health care, advancements were pushing AI forward. Marvin Minsky, cofounder of the Artificial Intelligence Laboratory at MIT, published *Society of the Mind* in 1987—organized into chapter-by-chapter puzzle pieces alluding to how systems can act together to make decisions.

While Minsky's book is abstract, a more tangible example of advancement of AI can be seen in robots. In fact, an early manifestation of self-driving car technology was evidenced by ALVINN, a project led by Dean Pomerleau of Carnegie Mellon. The technology responsible for ALVINN (Autonomous Land Vehicle In a Neural Network) was based on neural networks. As early as the late 1980s, Pomerleau and others demonstrated that a vehicle could be programmed to learn from images of roads and could drive itself using only a camera.

Despite advances in AI technology in the 1980s, a sense of skepticism and disillusionment thwarted support and funding for large-scale AI projects such as FGCS. The reduction in funding for projects explicitly related to AI even caused a tendency for those working in the field to select new terms for the science they were pursuing, and as the decade progressed, public opinion concluded that the aspirations for AI were not

---

26 Edward Shortliffe. "Artificial Intelligence in Medicine: Weighing the Accomplishments, Hype, and Promise." *IMIA Yearbook of Medical Informatics*, (2019): 257.

yet achieved, given slower than anticipated progress and high complexity of projects.[27]

While funding slowed and public enthusiasm for AI projects waned, progress continued in the fields of robotics and decision systems, among other areas. And in the early 1990s, the journal *Artificial Intelligence in Medicine* emerged. At MIT, Rodney Brooks and others created a humanoid robot called Cog, whose torso was capable of twenty-one degrees of freedom. Their work began in the summer of 1993, with the scientific goal of understanding human cognition. Yoky Matsuoka, a former VP at Google Health, studied robotics at MIT under Rodney Brooks.

Other notable AI advancements in the 1990s included development of the chess program, Deep Blue, which beat world chess champion Garry Kasparov in 1997. That same year, NASA's first autonomous robotics system, the Sojourner rover, was deployed on Mars as part of NASA's Pathfinder mission. And in 1998, Larry Page and Sergey Brin officially launched Google.

Today, we can observe enormous momentum behind development of AI technologies, and funding for the development of AI technology applied to health care has grown. A convergence is occurring. Technical advances are being matched with a robust enthusiasm for the potential benefits of applying AI to health care problems, supported by increased funding (private and public), and kept in check by healthy skepticism

---

27 Brender J. Handbook of evaluation methods for health informatics. Burlington, MA: Elsevier Academic Press 2006.

and caution toward potential misuses or biases. However, given the ability of AI to automate some processes, one should be careful not to minimize the role of medical providers and their responsibility. While some routine medical tasks and communication will be automated and augmented by AI, physicians and nurses are not rule-generators. Even in primary care where most of the research is ongoing, diagnoses can be complex, and human compassion is integral to the medicine.

WHAT CAN WE EXPECT NEXT?

Yuval Noah Harari, best-selling author of *Sapiens*, *Homo Deus*, and *21 Lessons for the 21st Century*, predicts that AI doctors will probably replace primary care doctors who focus on routine activities, such as diagnosing known diseases and administering familiar treatments.[28] Although his opinion is not the prevailing one within medicine, his comment raises a number of pertinent questions.

Will we see increased use of telemedicine to deliver primary care? Absolutely.

Will narrow AI algorithms be implemented to assist in clinical decision-making? Definitely.

Will human doctors be replaced by autonomous robots who have equal emotional intelligence, communication abilities, and domain expertise? Unlikely (at least not in the near future).

---

28 Yuval Noah Harari, *21 Lessons for the 21st Century*, Spiegel & Garu, 2018.

This is a brief history, and as Andrew Ng keenly points out, the momentum for the field has just begun to grow. To understand how these applications actually lead to improved health outcomes and affect medical decision-making, a fundamental understanding of the mechanics of artificial intelligence is helpful. For example: although neural networks have been used in the development of autonomous vehicles, what are they, and how could they be applied to health care? Many of us have heard of companies like 23andMe, Fitbit, Oscar, and Flatiron Health. All of these companies use AI to facilitate health care delivery. To better understand how your 23andMe results are informed by AI and enable more informed conversations with your doctor, who may use an AI tool to schedule your next appointment, a disentanglement of AI concepts is useful and will go a long way, as AI becomes increasingly influential in modern day health care.

CHAPTER 2:

ESSENTIAL AI AND MACHINE LEARNING CONCEPTS

AI is going to be more impactful than the invention of the personal computer and the spread of mobile phones into your pocket.

—JEFF DEAN, GOOGLE SENIOR FELLOW[29]

Whether you're standing in line for a cup of coffee, checking your email while riding the metro, or having dinner with family, you've probably overheard or discussed AI and machine learning. AI principles and methods are transferable across industries, but as a consumer of health care, you will find it increasingly valuable to know these terms when interacting with the health care system. The ways in which AI is impacting health care are often invisible to the patient (and even the provider in some cases). In other words, the patient probably won't see the underlying data used to train a machine learning algorithm or know which Python libraries were imported to create the predictive models.

---

29 Jeff Dean, "How Will Artificial Intelligence Affect Your Life," video, TEDXLA, accessed on March 31, 2020.

Most patients probably won't care about these details. However, some knowledge of how models are created is necessary to identify potential ways bias is introduced and will facilitate dialogue and accountability between patient and provider and between provider and developer. Since the use of AI in medicine is new and gaining momentum, the technical dialogue between patient and provider will also evolve and may become more technical. Understanding how these tools work will help us better understand the care we are receiving.

Many of the programming languages and tools used to build AI are open-source. This means that programming languages and technical infrastructure are transparent to all and accessible by a global community of software developers who write and evaluate code. Companies still maintain intellectual rights over the technology they produce but are increasingly using open-source tools like Python, R, and Linux. The open-source global community now includes support from large companies like Google, Amazon, and Microsoft, which are significantly contributing to many of the AI programming tools used in health care, such as Google Colab, Jupyter Notebooks, Tensorflow, Keras, and PyTorch.

Microsoft's acquisition of GitHub is one example that illustrates the value of open-source tools and the increased participation of tech giants in the open-source community. GitHub is the world's most popular platform for open-source projects and is used by approximately 40 million developers and 1.5 million companies worldwide to share and edit code. In 2018, Microsoft acquired GitHub for $7.5 billion in Microsoft stock, and the agreement allows GitHub to operate independently to continue providing an open platform for supporting any operating system and programming language of the programmer's choosing.[30] Companies' development of AI with open-source programming tools is becoming increasingly mainstream.

While the tools are free and open-source, the programs developed using the tools can be proprietary, and there is still a learning curve to understanding how to use the open-source tools to develop AI. Two main learning curves are relevant to understanding how to create AI:

1. Learning how to program (i.e., with open-source tools like Julia, Python, R, and their specialized libraries).
2. Learning how to employ ML libraries correctly (i.e., understanding matrix multiplication, basic calculus, and backpropagation for neural networks that is carried out within those libraries).

We have many ways to learn how to program machine learning tools, ranging from traditional academic programs to online programs. In addition to the technical learning curves, medical domain knowledge needs to guide development and determine relevance to clinical problems. Most clinical physicians are not computer programmers, so most of the machine learning tools supporting health care are developed within teams of health care providers and computer programmers. A machine learning engineer can develop accurate and efficient machine learning algorithms, such as

---

30   "Microsoft to acquire GitHub for $7.5 billion," Microsoft News Center, June 4, 2018, accessed on September 18, 2019.

convolutional neural networks (CNNs), which are a class of neural networks now popular for image analysis and classification. In medicine, CNNs can be designed to understand medical images, such as MRI scans and pathology images. A machine learning engineer can create a well-performing CNN, but domain knowledge in medicine is still needed for context and to evaluate clinical relevance.

With that said, data scientists have created AI algorithms that can predict if a given pathology image contains cancerous cells and if shadows within an MRI suggest the presence of tumors. Sometimes these algorithms perform as well as if not better than physicians. For example, a recent study by Google Health demonstrated the ability of an AI system to outperform radiologists in detecting breast cancer in a sample of data representing patients in the United States and United Kingdom.[31] The Google Health team, in collaboration with medical researchers in the US and UK, trained an AI tool on mammograms from about ninety thousand women and tested the tool on approximately thirty thousand new mammograms. Compared to review by radiologists with varying years of experience and fellowship training, the AI system showed a reduction of 5.7 percent (US) and 1.2 percent (UK) in false positives and a reduction of 9.4 percent and 2.7 percent in false negatives.[32] We should note that AI tools like the one by Google Health are developed with the guidance of physicians trained to understand the difference

31 Ian Sample, "AI system outperforms experts in spotting breast cancer," The Guardian, accessed on January 10, 2020.

32 Scott McKinney, et al, "International evaluation of an AI system for breast cancer screening." *Nature* 755 (2020): 89.

between healthy and cancerous tissue, not in their absence, and the tool is intended to reduce the workload of the physician since results are often reviewed multiple times or by multiple physicians. The study also shows that the process of developing and using AI technology may be both complex and expensive.

While the code developed by the Google Health team is not made publicly available due to infrastructure and hardware dependencies, the authors mention use of Tensorflow, a commonly used Python library for deep learning, and ensembling of three deep learning models. (In machine learning, ensembling is a technique that takes the predictions of many individual models and combines them to make a single prediction.) One form of deep learning, convolutional neural networks (CNNs), is used in image analysis to identify various stages of healthy and diseased tissue to support medical diagnosis.

A CNN is arguably the most important technique in deep learning and has been around for decades. It was popularized by a 2012 publication describing a CNN used for image classification.[33] Neural networks are programmatic abstractions of biological neurons, as shown in Figure 2.1. Perceptrons are the basic building blocks of neural networks, which generate a decision (in the form of a binary output) based on their input. Deep neural networks contain multiple layers of perceptrons, as shown in Figure 2.2.

---

33 Alex Krizhevsky, et al, "ImageNet Classification with Deep Convolutional Neural Networks," Neural Information Processing Systems.

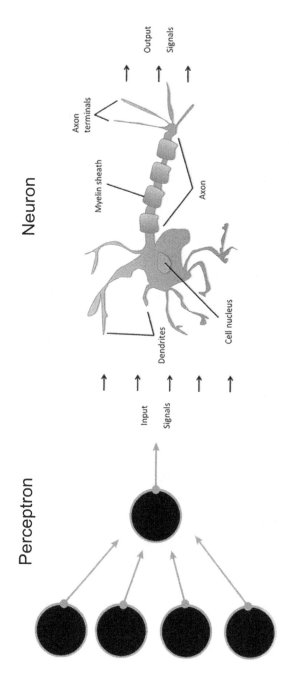

Figure 2.1: On the left, a perceptron, the building block of neural networks. On the right, the basic structure of a neuron. Adapted from the Udacity PyTorch Scholarship Challenge Nanodegree Program.

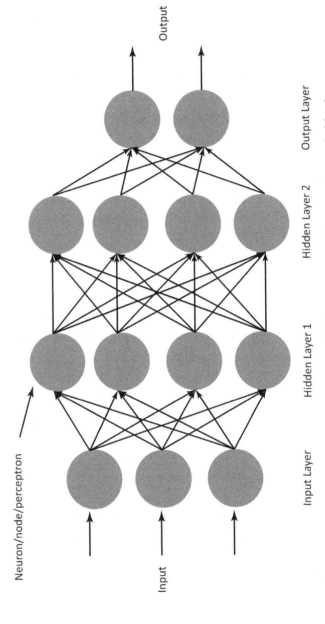

Figure 2.2: A deep neural network consists of a multilayer perceptron with two or more hidden layers.

As humans, we learn from patterns and experiences; similarly, neural networks and CNNs are designed to understand tiny nuances in data. As part of the learning process, neural networks are constructed of layers, where each layer becomes more complex. CNNs trained on image data can understand differences on the level of the pixel, and such granular details are important when understanding density changes in the MRI scans used by the Google Health team identifying breast cancer, for example. Computational power has enabled more widespread use of CNNs, and many open-source libraries (such as Tensorflow) allow the programmer to optimize parameters of the CNN to understand disease progression in pathology images.

The technical barriers of developing high-performing AI tools are decreasing thanks to individuals like Josh Gordon, a developer advocate for Google who leads training sessions on complex AI topics, and Jim Liew, an associate professor at Johns Hopkins who teaches courses on artificial intelligence and who has supported hundreds of students in his classes and through their careers. Gordon believes people with introductory technical skills can learn to understand and program AI, and he has developed a series of informative and practical machine learning "recipes" that any novice programmer can follow.[34]

Gordon understands that people have difficulty learning new skills, especially if they are already working, going to school, or have received training in another field. This reality is faced by some of the medical researchers featured in later

---

34 *Google Developers.* "ML Recipe #1: Hello World."

chapters too; Stephane Helleringer, a demography researcher at Johns Hopkins who develops facial recognition tools to support public health, acknowledges the hurdle of learning AI concepts after having studied traditional statistics and not AI or computer science.

Liew also recognizes that AI has become much more accessible since his entry to the field in 2012, following a career in quantitative finance, and that the industry has built on decades of work, with a few AI winters along the way. Liew believes any people who have taken courses in linear algebra and calculus have the right tools to understand the mechanics of AI and to train themselves if they have a desire to learn. He warns that people often skip the foundational layers of learning AI and can get into trouble as they lose intuition when the machine learning models become more complex. In other words, Liew advises people to dive in and start writing code as soon as possible, but to master the basics (i.e., linear algebra, matrix multiplication, and the inner workings of perceptrons) before working with more advanced topics.

ARTIFICIAL INTELLIGENCE (AI)

Artificial intelligence (AI) is a broad collection of tools and methods that enables computers to understand patterns. These tools and methods include mathematics, computer science, and logic. AI originated from mathematical concepts and ideas first articulated and practiced decades ago that have survived multiple AI winters. AI has been applied across diverse industries, and while health care is the focus of this book, AI touches transportation, energy, and even the niche use case of developing a neural network to sort cucumbers at one Japanese cucumber farm.[35] In energy, algorithms are trained on wind data to optimize the angle of wind turbines to boost energy output and increase revenues.[36]

AI consists of two broad categories: narrow and general.

NARROW AI

Narrow AI, or "weak AI," consists of the algorithms designed to solve one specific problem. This is the type of AI that includes use of machine learning algorithms to predict stock prices and patient diagnoses, and even to sort cucumbers. One notable example of narrow AI is AlphaGo—a machine learning algorithm created by DeepMind (now Google) to play the board game Go. Invented in China over two thousand years ago, Go is a two-player abstract strategy game played on a nineteen-by-nineteen grid of black lines. Each player has pieces, called stones, and the player who occupies the most space on the board wins. Compared to chess, Go is a much more complex game; in chess, the first player has twenty possible moves, compared to 361 in Go.[37] AlphaGo became famous for its ability to beat a world title Go player, Lee Sedol, in a series of matches in 2016. Sedol remarked, "I thought AlphaGo was based on probability calculations and

35 Anthony Cuthbertson, "How Artificial Intelligence is Helping Japanese Cucumber Farmers," Newsweek, accessed on March 31, 2020.

36 Peter Fairley, "Algorithms Help Turbines Share the Wind," IEEE Spectrum, July 1, 2019.

37 "A Comparison of Chess and Go," British Go Association, accessed on August 18, 2019.

that it was merely a machine. But when I saw this move, I changed my mind. Surely, AlphaGo is creative."[38]

And while Sedol observed creativity in the way AlphaGo played Go, what makes AlphaGo an example of narrow AI is its inability to be applied to other tasks, like playing a game of chess or tic-tac-toe. Another popular example of narrow AI was seen two decades earlier, also in the field of games. In 1997, IBM's chess player "Deep Blue" beat Russian chess grandmaster Garry Kasparov. While both of these examples of (narrow) AI are impressive, their applications are specific to Go and chess, respectively, and have not been extended to other "problems" due to their specificity. This is the nature of narrow AI.

GENERAL AI

General AI is the branch of AI that mimics human intelligence. This type of AI readily comes to mind when we think about movies like *Ex Machina*, *Interstellar*, *The Matrix*, and *Terminator*. In an interview, Elon Musk warns that "if humanity collectively decides that creating digital superintelligence is the right move, then we should do so very carefully" and that the single biggest and most pressing existential crisis we face is the advent of digital superintelligence and ensuring that its role is symbiotic with humanity.[39] As of this writing, the sophistication of AI from those movies is still in a distant and hopefully more compassionate future. General AI includes the computer programs that enable nonhuman

---

38 "AlphaGo," DeepMind, accessed on October 10, 2019.

39 *Good Dog*, "Elon Musk's Last Warning About Artificial Intelligence."

entities to perform, react, and adapt like humans, such as virtual avatars. While there is a lack of consensus on a definition of General AI, some computer algorithms are capable of mimicking human intelligence by reasoning and solving problems on their own and applying previously acquired knowledge to completely new problems. General AI is also known as "strong AI" in academic circles.

A FEW MORE DEFINITIONS

The health care machine learning tools created today are trained on historical medical data, often de-identified and aggregated from large populations. Machine learning models work by recognizing patterns in data. After the model is constructed, it is trained on historical data and tested on new data to predict an outcome. As we'll learn in the following chapters, most of the uses of AI in health care are focused on enhancing an existing process—such as improving the accuracy of pathology diagnoses or predicting the likelihood that a patient will require readmission to the hospital. In using curated data, the focus in health care has been the implementation of narrow AI to solve diagnostic, imaging, and administrative problems.

Narrow AI tools are developed to decipher patterns from years of historical patient records from large populations of patients, from genetic sequences, from years of doctor's notes, and from health-related images such as x-rays and histologic slides obtained from surgical specimens and biopsies. From the patterns found in these large quantities of data, AI tools typically generate the likelihood of an outcome or produce some classification, such as malignant or benign tissue. Health care AI tools can show you the likelihood that a specific patient will develop a specific disease or that a specific patient will need to reschedule their appointment; they can also categorize a tissue pathology image as healthy or cancerous.

We will see examples of companies, like Proscia and macro-eyes, that use narrow AI to improve the process of making pathology diagnoses and to optimize patient scheduling, respectively.

MACHINE LEARNING

AI and **machine learning** are closely related terms often used interchangeably. Figure 2.3 below illustrates how AI is the broad term that encompasses many subtypes of methods that build nonhuman intelligence. Machine learning is one of those methods and is applied in both narrow and general AI.

Andrew Ng, an expert in AI, offers two definitions for machine learning in his Coursera class on machine learning. Ng is known for his role cofounding the online learning platform Coursera, which is arguably democratizing nonformal education globally by offering many courses for free or at a low cost. Ng cofounded deeplearning.ai, an online platform for free or low-cost courses that teach deep learning. For an *informal* definition, Ng turns to computer scientist Arthur Samuel, who describes machine learning as "the field of study that gives computers the ability to learn without being explicitly programmed." Samuel was a computer scientist and early pioneer of artificial intelligence and is most known for his work in computer checkers in the 1940s and '50s.

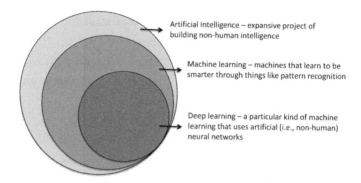

Artificial Intelligence – expansive project of building non-human intelligence

Machine learning – machines that learn to be smarter through things like pattern recognition

Deep learning – a particular kind of machine learning that uses artificial (i.e., non-human) neural networks

Figure 2.3: Artificial intelligence includes multiple subcategories, including machine learning and deep learning. Adapted from "How Will Artificial Intelligence Affect Your Life" by Google's Jeff Dean.[40]

A more *modern* definition comes from one of Ng's colleagues, Tom Mitchell: "A computer program is said to learn from experience E with respect to some class of tasks T and performance measure P, if its performance at tasks in T, as measured by P, improves with experience E." Mitchell is author of the textbook *Machine Learning* (1997) and a former chair of the machine learning department at Carnegie Mellon University.

The second definition is complex, so Ng offers the following example of checkers to define the terms:

E = the experience of playing many games of checkers
T = the task of playing checkers
P = the probability that the program will win the next game

---

40 Jeff Dean, "How Will Artificial Intelligence Affect Your Life," TEDXLA, accessed on March 31, 2020.

These definitions are relevant to classical machine learning, which is responsible for many of the narrow AI tools developed in health care. Classical machine learning consists of supervised learning, unsupervised learning, and reinforcement learning.

CLASSICAL MACHINE LEARNING

SUPERVISED LEARNING

The workhorse of machine learning is arguably **supervised learning**. This branch of machine learning relies on data that are already labeled with known classification. Outside of health care, email spam filters are a popular example of supervised learning. When you move a spam email into your spam folder, you are classifying that email as spam. A supervised algorithm learns the pattern of those spam emails based on things like sender, receiver, and subject line, which represent predictive features. When a new email reaches your inbox, the algorithm can classify that email as spam or not spam and direct it to the respective folder in your inbox. These classified data are called training data, as the machine learning algorithm trains itself on known classifications. In health care, supervised learning algorithms can be developed to predict clinical outcomes and diagnoses using thousands of predictive features, including historical medical data, medications, laboratory tests, and clinical procedures.

Even with years of training data for millions of individuals, the algorithms are not perfect; important emails occasionally get directed to your spam folder, and sometimes a spam email finds its way into your inbox. In other words, spam detection is imperfect, as are supervised learning algorithms developed for health care. False positives occur when a legitimate email is classified as spam while false negatives occur when a spam email is classified as regular email. The fallible nature of AI lends itself to a variety of ethical considerations specific to health care, as we'll see in later chapters.

UNSUPERVISED LEARNING

While supervised learning depends on the availability of labeled data, unsupervised learning uses data that are unlabeled. Unsupervised learning is employed to cluster data based on similar traits and to find patterns in data. We'll learn about some examples of unsupervised learning in health care, namely in genetics, but also for clustering populations of individuals based on similar characteristics.

Researchers might use unsupervised learning methods to classify cellular images based on their histopathology; given a large enough sample size, cells of similar disease progression will appear similar to each other. The machine learning researcher can select (and optimize) the number of clusters from the sample set, identifying four different grades of cancer, for example.

REINFORCEMENT LEARNING

The third type of classical machine learning—**reinforcement learning**—should be mentioned, and while examples of reinforcement learning applied to health care exist, currently this form of machine learning is primarily known for its role in self-driving cars and virtual gaming. Reinforcement learning algorithms collect observations from an agent, like a car, and evaluate if the action was successful based on predetermined criteria. In this sense, the agent (i.e., car) is learning from its surroundings. As an example, reinforcement learning algorithms support Tesla's AutoPilot feature, which keeps the car in the lane and a safe distance from surrounding vehicles. As the car drives on AutoPilot, data gathered from live camera sensors are processed by CNNs.[41] Using the live photos gathered by multiple cameras, the car learns from its interactions with its surroundings. Is the car staying in its lane? Did the car drive too closely to the curb? Was the car centered within its lane?

While each car learns on its own, the real power of reinforcement learning is achieved in aggregate. Thousands of Teslas running AutoPilot send feedback to Tesla's servers and inform the reinforcement learning algorithms on how well a car is driving to retrain and improve the model for future software enhancements that are pushed out to Tesla's fleet. This feedback loop improves the algorithm and ultimately improves the self-driving function of the car.

The health care field offers some limited research applications of reinforcement learning, including optimization of mechanical ventilation. One study from researchers at Princeton University and the University of Pennsylvania developed an algorithm to wean intensive care unit patients from mechanical ventilators.[42] Using historical data, the algorithm

---

41 *PyTorch*. "Pytorch at Tesla."

42 Niranjani Prasad, et al, "A Reinforcement Learning Approach to Weaning of Mechanical Ventilation in Intensive Care Units," Princeton University, Print.

was capable of recommending extubation time and sedation levels that on average outperformed clinical practice and could help inform improved policies.

Two other types of machine learning are important to cover outside of classical machine learning: neural networks and natural language processing.

NEURAL NETWORKS

Neural networks are a powerful type of machine learning based loosely on the functioning of neurons and the ways in which neurons communicate with each other. Multiple types of neural networks exist, including convolutional neural networks and recurrent neural networks, and multiple programming tools are used to apply those methods. The advantage of neural networks is the ability to see relationships among seemingly disparate variables and to train a computer to make patterns. Many of the applications of neural networks—for health care and otherwise—are based on images. The field of pathology lends itself to use of neural networks since it is a field based heavily on optics data.

NATURAL LANGUAGE PROCESSING (NLP)

Natural language processing is the field of machine learning focused on teaching computers how to systematically extract meaning from text data. In a traditional and broad sense, computers are trained to ingest some corpus of text, remove filler content and punctuation, and look for text of interest. Within health care, NLP is a valuable tool used to understand medical record data since many of the data contained within EHR systems are structured text and machine-readable. However, estimates suggest only about 75 percent of EHR data are accurate. Notes documented by the provider may not be complete, may reflect just the specialty of the physician, and are typically based only on what is billable. In other words, while text-based notes are a rich source of data, they tell a partial story.

HOW ARE DIFFERENT TYPES OF MACHINE LEARNING USED IN HEALTH CARE?

SUPERVISED LEARNING IN HEALTH CARE

Recall that supervised learning is arguably the most important and widely used type of machine learning. This type of machine learning is used in regression and classification and when the data are already labeled. Supervised learning algorithms can be used to predict a doctor's diagnosis given previous clinical and behavioral data. These diagnosis data are considered "labeled" since we already know the diagnosis for the patient and factors associated with the diagnosis, such as the patient's demographic data, vital signs, laboratory results, and history of prescribed medications. Tens of thousands of labeled features in the data can be relevant to the prediction. However, frequently only a handful or small number of these variables actually provide predictive power. Selecting the most important features is one of the more time-consuming steps of creating a supervised learning algorithm and requires a thoughtful approach to avoid bias in the prediction model.

Often, supervised learning algorithms are combined with other types of machine learning algorithms. Demography researcher Stephane Helleringer of Johns Hopkins uses supervised learning and computer vision to predict the age of individuals in rural Senegal using their facial photographs. Supervised learning methods were employed to model the relationship between facial features extracted from images and age while computer vision tools were used to train a computer how to extract information from photographs in a machine-readable format.

UNSUPERVISED LEARNING IN HEALTH CARE

Unsupervised learning is a form of learning without labels. Unsupervised learning discovers hidden patterns within the data by finding ways to create groups within the data based on similar characteristics (clustering), taking a large dataset with hundreds of features and compressing the dataset into a more manageable size (dimensionality reduction), and finding unusual patterns within data (anomaly detection). Unsupervised learning algorithms often complement other types of machine learning. For example, a dataset can first be simplified with a dimensionality reduction technique before using it to train a supervised learning classifier.

In health care, unsupervised learning is helpful in the field of genomics, especially when analyzing the genomes of thousands or millions of patients. The human genome contains around thirty thousand distinct genes whose expression are highly regulated by information inside the cell (i.e., cellular damage) and outside the cell (i.e., nutrients, toxins, signals from other cells). The genes are constructed by base pairs, and chromosomes contain multiple genes. For context, the human genome contains about three billion base pairs. Analyzing genetic data from thousands of patients creates vast amounts of data fit for unsupervised learning techniques, as little is actually curated and labeled like clinical data.

Analyzing human genome DNA has become easier thanks to advances in genomic sequencing, and much is still unknown about how changes in gene expression lead to disease. DNA microarray is a technique used by scientists to quantify the level of expression of genes; it can reveal mutations in genes that lead to disease. With DNA microarray data, unsupervised learning algorithms are used to group patients by how much of a gene is expressed. Revealing hidden genomic relationships facilitates more effective clinical trials because it can uncover genes that affect whether subsets of patients will respond differently to a medication.

NEURAL NETWORKS IN HEALTH CARE

Neural networks have become popular with respect to image-based applications. In a later chapter, we'll see an example in pathology that relies on this type of AI. But in short, the pathologist relies on using microscopes to read slides of biopsied tissue to determine the severity or absence of disease based on tissue morphology. Multiple groups of scientists and computer programmers are finding ways to use AI techniques, including neural networks, to make sense of vast amounts of pathology images collected from thousands of patients. Technology based on neural networks that learns from thousands of diverse pathology cases is becoming an important tool pathologists use to expedite the process of making an accurate diagnosis.

Neural networks excel at finding patterns among disparate and unknown features in ways that supervised learning algorithms cannot. In many cases, these features are factors found within images, perhaps small changes in density or subtle color gradients that a human physician could easily overlook or ignore.

Several partnerships between industry and academic medical research centers have produced meaningful advances using neural networks. As one example, researchers at Google used neural networks in the detection of diabetic eye disease, based on thousands of images of the retina.[43,44] In another example, using EHR data consisting of over forty-six billion data points, researchers at Google, University of California–San Francisco, and the University of Chicago demonstrated that neural networks can accurately predict the sequence of events during a patient encounter.[45,46] These events included discharge from the hospital and prescription of medications. As a third example, researchers at Google, Stanford University, New York University, and Northwestern University used neural networks to develop lung cancer screening tools based on over forty-five thousand de-identified chest CT screening cases and compared their results to board certified

43 "Seeing Potential: How a team at Google is using AI to help doctors prevent blindness in diabetes," Google, accessed on March 20, 2020.

44 Lily Peng, "Deep Learning for Detection of Diabetic Eye Disease," Google AI Blog, 2016, accessed on October 2, 2019.

45 Alvin Rajkomar and Eyal Oren"Deep Learning for Electronic Health Records," Google AI Blog, accessed on March 31, 2020.

46 Alvin Rajkomar, et al, "Scalable and accurate deep learning with electronic health records," npj Digital Med 1, 18 (2018).

radiologists.[47,48] The tool performed on par with the radiologists for detection of cancerous lesions; it detected 5 percent more cancer cases and reduced the false-positive error rate by more than 11 percent compared to unassisted radiologists.

NATURAL LANGUAGE PROCESSING (NLP) IN HEALTH CARE

The use of **NLP** in health care is fairly recent. Beginning with a dream in 2004 from former President George W. Bush and continued later by former President Barack Obama that all patients have an electronic health record,[49] hospital systems and tech entrepreneurs have found ways to collect health data in formats that machine learning tools can understand. (And thanks to the Obama HITECH Act, I received a grant to pursue graduate studies in public health informatics.)

Previous methods of data entry were based on handwritten charts and notes, but the transition to electronic data storage has not been entirely free of difficulty. As quotidian as it may now sound, a significant barrier to adopting EHR technology was the need to train health care providers to use computers to enter medical notes and observations into a computer. Workflows were altered and disrupted, and the more rigid method of data entry (compared to paper and

---

47   Diego Ardila, et al, "End-to-end lung cancer screening with three-dimensional deep learning on low-dose chest computed tomography," *Nature Medicine*, 25 (2019): 954.

48   Shravya Shetty, "A promising step forward for predicting lung cancer." Google, accessed on June 2, 2019.

49   KMTS, "What is the EMR Mandate?" Kristin Muller Transcription, accessed on March 31, 2020.

pencil) represented a significant departure from the use of free-form text. Handwritten text notes have been replaced by checkboxes, limited use of typed text, and standardized codes. These codes include ICD (International Statistical Classification of Diseases) codes, which are currently in their tenth edition and whose development has been supported by the World Health Organization since the 1940s.

Data standards imposed by the transition to EHRs arguably benefited all types of machine learning, especially NLP. Since the structured text available within EHR systems has become increasingly reliable, NLP is used to search the structured text systematically. Research groups are using NLP to aid in finding cohorts of rheumatoid arthritis patients by searching ICD codes and prescription medications along with information from different types of notes, such as radiology reports, pathology reports, and discharge summaries.[50,51] Once the techniques are proven on one EHR system, they can be replicated at other institutions across millions of patients, as was shown at Vanderbilt and Northwestern.[52] Care must be taken to acknowledge and mitigate biases inherent to initial development, as patient populations can radically differ across institutions. The composition of training data at one

50   "NLP," Massachusetts Institute of Technology, accessed on March 31, 2020.

51   Katherine Liao, et al, "Electronic Medical Records for Discovery Research in Rheumatoid Arthritis." Arthritis Care & Research 62, no. 8 (2010): 1120.

52   Robert Carroll, et al, "Portability of an algorithm to identify rheumatoid arthritis in electronic health records." Journal of the American Medical Informatics Association 19 (2012): e162.

institution may not completely represent the patient population at another institution. Interoperability of health records (and use of machine learning tools to analyze those records) across institutions is easier when those institutions share the same EHR vendor, as evidenced by a handful of EHR vendors who dominate the space.

FROM IDEAS TO REALITY

Consider these paragraphs a quick primer on AI, as other forms of AI exist and the effort required to create accurate AI tools is not insignificant. While each type of machine learning has its own purposes and applications, the different kinds' uses are not mutually exclusive and are often combined within the same project.

As we will find, developing these tools requires a thoughtful process and sometimes years of devoted research. Implementing these tools takes time too, particularly in a sensitive field like health care. In fact, many of the applied examples mentioned in this chapter are still in design, which means they are not yet used to influence clinical decision-making.

So, how do we apply these AI research ideas toward productive applications with a clinical impact? What will it take to bring theories into reality?

CHAPTER 3:

IDEA TO IMPLEMENTATION

———

Yesterday at lunch a friend asked me what tech trend he should pay attention to but was probably ignoring.

Without thinking much I said, "artificial intelligence," but having thought about that a bit more, I think it's probably right.

—SAM ALTMAN, CEO OF OPENAI AND FORMER PRESIDENT OF Y COMBINATOR[53]

AI ideas applied to health care can originate anywhere. Ideas begin in the mind of a curious college student, like David West, and blossom into well-funded companies. West is the founder of digital pathology company Proscia. Ideas are also generated in more systematic ways—in the offices of Google and Microsoft. And ideas for AI in health care can even take root in curious and driven individuals who transition to health care from other industries, like Benjamin Fels, who was a successful quantitative trader before founding health care AI company macro-eyes.

---

53   Sam Altman, "AI," accessed on February 17, 2020.

West, Fels, and others have defined and implemented action-able ideas. For a fortunate few, ideation can come easy and is ultimately the product of having a clear problem to solve, but ideation must occur in the context of some clinical prob-lem. Sometimes just hanging out with the right people and getting into an exploration mindset can serve as the catalyst to spark new ideas and conjure the gumption to take next steps. After all, identifying a specific problem and devising an approach are only two-thirds of the solution. Actually creating a prototype is the essential third leg. Implementing the idea requires motivation, validation, and funding before it is developed into a tangible form accessible to users.

In only a few years, AI has become a household term. While the froth and excitement of AI have led to a boom of devel-opment in the health care space, we risk eagerly sprinkling AI on problems that could more easily (or appropriately) be solved without it. Since AI has garnered a palpable hype, companies could potentially (and some do) implement AI in superficial ways merely for marketing benefit.

One successful framework that systematically identifies and supports emerging health ideas exists at Johns Hop-kins Health Care Solutions (JHHCS), a group led by Mark Cochran. I first met Cochran when I was supporting an open-source biobank management software application piloted by the gastroenterology division at the Johns Hop-kins School of Medicine and later adopted for enterprise use at the School of Medicine. The application had robust query capabilities, and with some training, the user could search for tissue samples belonging to a patient with specific conditions and know where the sample was stored. For example, the user could search for all available blood serum samples with volume greater than 0.5 mL for male patients between the ages of thirty and forty with a history of smoking; the results show that the specimens are stored in freezer A, shelf two, rack one, box five, and positions nine to twelve. While these query capabilities do not use AI, they have tremendous value to the researcher conducting clinical trials who needs to catalogue the research specimens. At a later date, these specimens can be systematically retrieved by searching against criteria related to patient demographics and diagnosis.

The search capabilities and the ability of the application to record custom, granular research data were of interest to Cochran and to a senior pharmaceutical executive interested in performing clinical trials at Johns Hopkins. I gave a demonstration of an early version of the application to Cochran and others. At the time, I was a part-time master of public health student at the Johns Hopkins Bloomberg School of Public Health and a member of the Hopkins Biotech Network—a student-led group that supports students interested in careers in biotechnology and hosts speaker series with researchers, entrepreneurs, and investors.

Later, some time after my biobanking presentation, I invited Cochran to give a presentation for the Hopkins Biotech Network. He spoke about his career path and the goals of Johns Hopkins Health Care Solutions, and he was very welcoming to questions and to learning about student projects. A few students even approached Cochran after his talk to ask if JHHCS would fund their idea. Later, we would talk about science and technology over the occasional beer in Fell's Point Baltimore.

At an earlier stage in his career before JHHCS, Cochran was tasked with visiting academic research labs and evaluating new biotechnology being developed by the labs for potential commercialization. Given his training in microbiology and immunology, he could evaluate the scientific rigor and legitimacy of research. With funds from his employer, he was poised to support research ideas with venture capital funding, if a profitable business case could be identified. JHHCS is run with a similar entrepreneurial approach: identify promising research ideas and find ways to profitably scale those ideas.

To scale scientific solutions developed during academic research, JHHCS uses the following three steps:

1. Identify successful programs that could reach and have a positive effect on a statistically relevant portion of the overall population and at a cost that at least could be sustainable at a price a client would be willing to pay.
2. Market to relevant client segments.
3. Demonstrate a return on investment to every client.

Following this model delivers benefits to the inventor or scientist, to the university, and to external stakeholders. And the model of JHHCS generates profit for Johns Hopkins. Approximately 60 percent of revenues generated across JHHCS projects are reinvested in R&D efforts at Johns Hopkins. Last year, of the $15 million in revenue generated by JHHCS projects, about $9 million were sent back to Johns Hopkins faculty departments to support their ideas.

Not all the ideas Cochran evaluates are rosy. Any idea a faculty member would like to advance commercially becomes their baby. Sometimes Cochran has to tell said faculty that their babies are ugly! The blunt truth may hurt, but it can be instructive to the faculty when he explains why their baby just isn't ready for prime time. He also warns to be careful of the "flavors of the month"—potential entrepreneurs who are hopping on a bandwagon but don't have the credibility or expertise to execute on their idea. Whenever Cochran looks at new products or technology, he thinks about how the new technology can be integrated into an existing process. He remarks that when it comes to health care, currently tens of thousands of software apps exist; a management problem becomes figuring out how to integrate multiple tools, even if they have good value. Cochran thinks the electronic health record is a good place to start, especially for AI-related ideas.

FROM ACADEMIA TO SCALE: POPULATION HEALTH ANALYTICS

One of the landmark successes of JHHCS is the Adjusted Clinical Groups (ACG) system, which is a health IT platform developed at the Johns Hopkins Bloomberg School of Public Health that models and predicts an individual's need for health care over time using existing data from medical claims, electronic medical records, and demographics.[54] ACG was initially developed to analyze health insurance claims data, whose workflow resembles the following steps:

1. A doctor prescribes the patient a medication.
2. The diagnosis code gets entered into the EHR.

---

54 "The Johns Hopkins ACG System: Decades of Impact on Population Health Research and Practice," The Johns Hopkins University, 2020.

3. An insurance company evaluates the prescription; if favorable, the insurance company generates a claim.
4. A hospital billing system evaluates the claim.

These data are available for millions of patient encounters at Johns Hopkins alone. The ACG system ingests data from insurance claims and then the system generates actionable insights for the individual patient and for the larger population of patients being analyzed. ACG can answer questions like: *What are some health risks for this one patient? What are the health trends among the group of patients? What is the cost of treatment for this patient? How much does a given state reimburse for the procedure or medication?* For employers, ACG addresses the question of which targeted care management and wellness programs you should consider in your population health management approach. In other words, given historical health data including billing, prescription medications, and comorbidities associated with a particular condition, ACG creates predictive models on the patient and population levels.

The ACG system has undergone many version upgrades over its thirty years on the market as a population health management tool. Its first enhancement was the ability of the system to analyze prescription drug information. A later upgrade integrated access to the electronic medical record. Cochran points out that an ongoing key to the success of ACG is working closely with "data junkies who love data," meaning the data scientists and statisticians who create computer programs needed to understand data and who establish the interfaces between clinical and research systems.

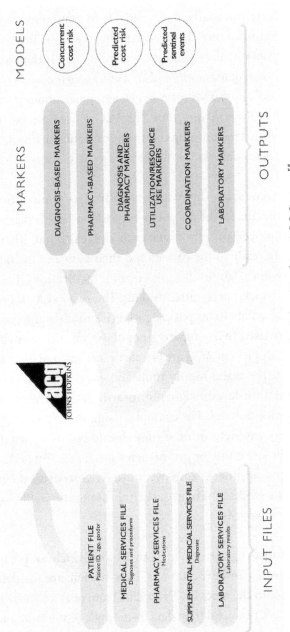

MODELS

- Concurrent cost risk
- Predicted cost risk
- Predicted sentinel events

MARKERS

- DIAGNOSIS-BASED MARKERS
- PHARMACY-BASED MARKERS
- DIAGNOSIS AND PHARMACY MARKERS
- UTILIZATION/RESOURCE USE MARKERS
- COORDINATION MARKERS
- LABORATORY MARKERS

OUTPUTS

INPUT FILES

- PATIENT FILE
  Patient ID, age, gender
- MEDICAL SERVICES FILE
  Diagnoses and procedures
- PHARMACY SERVICES FILE
  Medications
- SUPPLEMENTAL MEDICAL SERVICES FILE
  Diagnoses
- LABORATORY SERVICES FILE
  Laboratory results

Figure 3.1: Input files, outputs, and models relevant to the Johns Hopkins ACG System.[55]

55 Ibid.

These researchers conduct experiments by combining data-sets, such as insurance claims and medical records. Together with physicians, they generate questions about the data: *Does inclusion of the additional dataset(s) help the predictive model? Could any existing peer-reviewed publications guide the group in the right direction?* For ACG, these data experiments revealed relationships between insurance claims data and pharmacy data that provide value to ACG users.

In its current state, the ACG system ingests many forms of data specific to the adopter—typically a health plan, a large employer, or a provider such as HealthStat. These input data relate to the patient and their care and include demographics, lab results, prescription medications, EHR data, and social determinants data. The ACG system processes these data to output potential risk models and flags, which are used in a company's population health strategy. Current adopters of ACG are primarily self-insured employers of one thousand to fifty thousand employees who use its population-level insights to inform data-driven company health policies. For example, using data from ACG, employers can determine if they should consider installing an on-site clinic or pre-diabetes programs. By taking a proactive approach, employers use ACG to drive down their costs while simultaneously improving the wellbeing of their employees.

When evaluating the results of an AI tool, Cochran is cautious of biases and expectations. How reliable are the data that feed into the model? Claims data from multiple providers are more powerful than data from single physicians who may be operating under personal biases.

The progression of the ACG system followed that of many other successful enterprise health analytics tools. It started out small, as a predictive tool with only a single dataset that addressed a predictive problem. Once the initial concept was successful, the team explored additional datasets to include, based on feedback from stakeholders and perceived value of the new features. Today, ACG is used in nearly thirty countries and impacts over two hundred million people. The impressive expansion of ACG would not have been possible had an initial idea not been supported, tested and validated, and then deployed with funding. Let's take a closer look at the steps.

STEP 1: IDENTIFY A PROBLEM

Ideation can stem from observing a clinical procedure or participating in a hackathon. David West, founder of a digital pathology company, Proscia, will show us how ideation can be nurtured from a productive combination of a fascination and need. All successful AI projects start with a well-defined problem to solve. Another example comes from the field of demography.

Stephane Helleringer of the Johns Hopkins Bloomberg School of Public Health is interested in measuring demographics in areas of the world where infrastructure does not exist to reliably collect population demographics, such as rural Senegal. For Helleringer, the problem to solve was clear. How do we generate demographic information with unreliable infrastructure and missing historical data? Even communicating with Helleringer demonstrated one of the material challenges he faces daily—due to a lack of stable internet, we had to conduct our interview through emails instead of a phone call or video conference.

Demographics are key to delivering good health care and serve as the foundation for evidence-based treatment, especially for populations. Treatment of hypertension for a fifty-year-old differs from that for a sixty-five-year-old. Even traditional diagnoses made without the assistance of AI are based on patterns. Doctors learn from their experience and the collective experience of their colleagues during grand rounds and journal clubs. And of course, predictive tools like the ACG would have little value in population health analytics if they have to contend with large unknowns and gross estimations for the age of the population. Going back to Cochran's caution, can we trust the data? In this case, can we trust that the demographics being fed into a predictive model are accurate?

Helleringer studied social sciences and traditional statistics, yet he realizes that one of the barriers to implementing his machine learning ideas relates to training. Without sufficient training, researchers like Helleringer can't develop machine learning tools or evaluate their accuracy. For social scientists like Helleringer who are trained in standard statistical methods used to evaluate surveys and census data, the process of "upgrading" one's technical skill base is time-consuming. An understanding of how the machine learning model works is necessary for testing and validating.

STEP 2: BUILD AND TEST A PROTOTYPE

Ideation, followed by some initial programming, leads to an iterative process of building and testing the idea. An idea can be tested for both its business and technical soundness. From a business perspective, the AI tool should provide value to users, and the user should be able to understand it. From a technical perspective, the model needs to be evaluated for its accuracy and to reveal any biases in its predictions.

I learned lessons about testing and validation from Dr. Robert Miller. When I spoke with Dr. Miller, his passion and excitement for technology within health care were immediately apparent, yet he maintains a healthy skepticism for meaningful adoption. Given the nascent nature of AI applied to health care, Dr. Miller suggests that while we don't really understand where AI fits within the field, the current uses of machine learning in health care can be identified as "imperfect classifiers with nondeterministic algorithms that have a tendency for spurious error."

In other words, designing perfectly accurate machine learning classifiers is impossible, and each time the machine learning model is run (such as with neural networks or tree-based algorithms), the output differs slightly. Due to the imperfect nature of the classifiers and when nondeterministic algorithms are driving the calculations, seemingly random errors result. In the medical field, random errors are a huge red flag. Would I want my medical care dictated by a process whose output changes slightly after each run and in ways that are "spurious"? Does the spurious change in output reflect new information in the machine learning model? Or is the spurious change simply an error?

Hence, thoroughly testing and validating the AI tool is necessary and must be done with a good understanding of the underlying model. It also needs to be done under the guidance of domain expertise—namely, physicians and providers who have human understanding of the clinically relevant predictions being generated.

Even human experts cannot predict outcomes or classify with perfect accuracy. We make conclusions and judgments based on experiences and training. Similarly, machine learning tools are imperfect, but their errors are not well understood. Especially for neural networks, random forests, or other complex models, the source of error can be difficult to find and resolve.

Dr. Miller believes that people are not always aware of issues of spectrum and bias inherent to machine learning models.[56] He and others point out: is your patient training set representative of the patients you are going to test in the future? Sometimes this is not the case, especially in underrepresented patient populations. For example, if an algorithm is trained on data taken only from middle-aged white patients, and if your patient is a twenty-five-year-old black man, this algorithm might not be effective and might suffer from inherent bias. This is a key limitation and challenge, as a majority of algorithms use population datasets that might not be relevant to providing personalized care to the individual.

Determining the accuracy of machine learning tools begs the question: how do machine learning tools compare to

---

56 David Ransohoff and Alvan Feinstein. "Problems of Spectrum and Bias in Evaluating the Efficacy of Diagnostic Tests." *New England Journal of Medicine* 299, no.17 (1978):926.

humans? One commonly used metric for accuracy of machine learning models is the receiver operating characteristic (ROC) curve, whose origins are in radar research and engineering. The ROC curve is a technical measure and probably not something that strongly resonates with the typical patient; in Dr. Miller's words, "only engineers could come up with this." The ROC curve is constructed by plotting the true positive rate against the false positive rate, and it shows the trade-off between sensitivity and specificity. As Figure 3.2 demonstrates, a better performing model shows a ROC curve that hugs the top-left corner, which represents perfect sensitivity and specificity. The 45-degree line represents a random guess. Most ROC curves fall somewhere between the top-left corner and the 45-degree line.

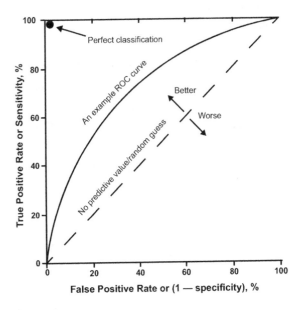

Figure 3.2: A ROC curve.

Use of the ROC dates back to approximately World War II, when ROC curves were used to help radar operators decide whether the radar signal was a sign of enemy aircraft or just noise, such as a flock of birds. The term has roots in Stanford and Silicon Valley as a consequence of the US Department of Defense's funding of microwave research after World War II. Today, ROC curves are used to evaluate machine learning algorithms across industries and is an easy way to compare different AI models. In health care, early use of ROCs caused enormous controversy. Radiologists were castigated if the accuracy of their diagnoses wasn't similar to points along the ROC. A conversation would go something like: *You shouldn't have this many false positives and negatives. If you're a good enough radiologist, you should be able to catch all of these diagnoses.* Radiologists were understandably agitated about this.

Quibbles about the ROC and whether a physician is "good enough" beg the question: what is good enough for a machine learning model? If you have a 90 percent true positive rate, is that good enough (and does the patient know)? Maybe for certain machine learning applications but not for others. If you have a ROC that reports a 95 percent true positive rate but 15 percent false positives, is that okay?

A foundational prerequisite to developing accurate machine learning models is the availability of well-understood and balanced data for training and testing. Unsurprisingly, 70 to 80 percent of the time needed to develop machine learning models is devoted to exploring, understanding, and formatting the data in ways that are suitable for training machine learning models.

As part of the process, data scientists measure the flaws and errors of their models. No machine learning model is perfect, regardless of its sophistication. In terms of errors, Dr. Miller points out the consequences of false positives, which may lead to the ordering of unnecessary procedures that can increase the anxiety for the patient and incur additional costs. Additionally, both false positive and false negative errors may lead to inappropriate management and potential harm to patients in some high-risk situations.

STEP 3: DEPLOY A PRODUCTION VERSION

The output of any AI tool needs to reach users. Typically, that output is rendered via an app on your cell phone or within a web page, either publicly or privately hosted. While displaying results may sound trivial, new branches of user experience design are emerging specifically to address the understandability of AI tools. What good is an output if the user doesn't understand the result, is highly mistrusting of the result, or some combination?

The software development life cycle includes a variety of colorful terms, including "deployment." The final step in making a software application available to users is when developers deploy the application into production, meaning the software application is available to their desired user base, often the public.

In a traditional software development life cycle, the research and ideation steps begin in protected environments that are still within the control of the developer and not yet available to the public. Development and test environments are two such preproduction environments, but many others exist. Testing and validation of the AI tool also occur in these preproduction environments, as shown in Figure 3.3.

The process highlighted in Figure 3.3 represents a traditional software development progression for enterprise applications. Some "low-code" methods are emerging that leverage cloud-provider infrastructure to significantly decrease the time it takes to develop and deploy an application to production, which can take weeks to months depending on the complexity of the application. Microsoft's Power Apps are one low-code solution that allows for rapid deployment of applications using cloud data.[57] Microsoft allows the developer to see how their machine learning application performs in real time when using APIs available through Microsoft Cognitive Services.

While the preproduction environments might be exciting and stimulating for the machine learning developer, the technical activity in these stages of development is usually too far into the weeds to be of interest to the user (such as the patient). During this phase, developers tweak hyperparameters, merge datasets, build and test APIs, do security testing, load testing, or write code for custom user interfaces. At this early stage, the AI tool itself is probably of little value to the user. For the AI tool to come alive for users and generate value, it needs to be embedded in an interface that is understandable to patients or to the provider—whoever is the end user of the application.

---

57   "Microsoft Power Apps on Azure." Microsoft, accessed on March 12, 2020.

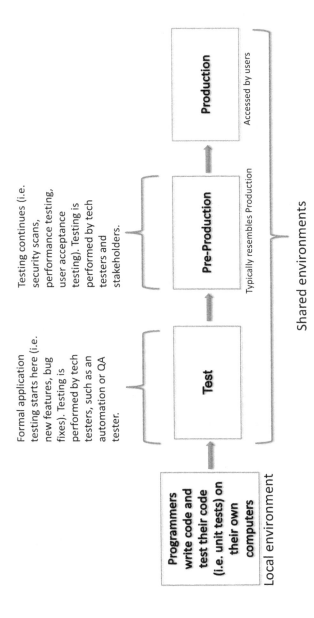

Figure 3.3: A basic workflow for software development showing local development and progression through pre-production environments.

Data scientists and machine learning engineers work with other programmers and user-experience designers who translate their technical models into interactive software applications. This transition is an art and a science, since it follows a structured process but also requires an understanding of how to best present information to the user given the user's motivations and preferences. Groups like Google are developing user-experience guidelines for the emerging field of "Explainable AI," which aims to provide a good understanding of machine learning models to a general audience.[58] This field didn't exist two years ago.

As we'll learn later, users of health care AI tools are diverse and include patients, providers, payers, and big pharma. One patient-focused application, Dosecast, is a good example of a predictive tool whose development followed the structure similar to the one outlined above.[59] We will learn a bit about Dosecast and the motivations for applying predictive analytics to prescription drug adherence later in the book.

While the development process outlined in Figure 3.3 is general, additional requirements unique to health care steer development of software and algorithms. HIPAA regulations and consent-of-use laws regarding health data impose constraints on which data can be used and how. As we will find, nontraditional, "alternative" forms of health data skirt the requirements for HIPAA protection and are becoming increasingly valuable in their role of developing AI tools.

---

58 "People + AI Guidebook: Designing Human-Centered AI Products," PAIR with Google, accessed on August 30, 2020.

59 Montuno Software, Homepage, accessed on October 20, 2019.

Time will tell if these alternative forms of health data may actually become the new "traditional," as personal devices and applications continue to capture health-related data. A seemingly endless supply of AI ideas exists for the person who clearly identifies a problem, follows the steps to deploying the solution, and understands how to handle health data ethically.

As we've seen so far, many of the health care AI ideas with the most impact on health care function behind the scenes. Like any good software tool, health care AI tools "just work." In other words, if the user of the tool is a patient, they typically don't see the hyperparameters tuning in the background, the pathway down a decision tree, or the mechanisms of back propagation. One digital pathology company, Proscia, uses deep learning and other AI methods to facilitate quicker and more accurate pathology diagnoses—a process that is invisible to the patient. Deep learning tools developed by BenevolentAI improve the speed of drug discovery. The patient does not see this process, but they stand to benefit from lower drug costs. One of the outcomes of the work at BenevolentAI is the creation of twenty-four drug candidates in just four years, when traditionally the process can take ten years.[60]

---

60   Saurav Patyal, "BenevolentAI: Revolutionizing drug discovery using Artificial Intelligence," HBS Digital Initiative, accessed on January 9, 2020.

PART 2:
OBSTACLES

CHAPTER 4:

ETHICAL AI

---

*I have lots of worries— the issue of privacy and security
of the data, about whether the AI algorithms are always
proved out with real patients, and about how AI might
worsen some inequities. Algorithms themselves are
not biased, but the data we put into those algorithms,
because they are chosen by humans, often are. However,
I don't think these are insoluble problems.*

—ERIC TOPOL, GENETICIST, PHYSICIAN,
AND AUTHOR OF *DEEP MEDICINE*[61]

When training the model, how do we define good and bad?
Machine learning algorithms and human decision-making
are both prone to biases. Human cognitive biases are mental
shortcuts that skew decision-making and reasoning, resulting in reasoning errors. Biases are innately human, and we
get in trouble and hurt others when our biases go unchecked
and result in prejudice, leading to favoring for or against a
person, group, or thing in an unfair way. Many flavors of

---

61 Alice Park, "Cardiologist Eric Topol on How AI Can Bring Humanity
Back to Medicine," *TIME Magazine*, accessed on January 11, 2020.

human cognitive biases exist: the bandwagon effect, stereo-typing, and selection bias, a few among many.

While the origins of biases in machine learning algo-rithms relate to the source of data, they can be subtle. Do the training data contain things the model should ignore? Are the training data complete? Without thoughtful and objective code review, even the inherent cognitive biases of the human computer programmer can cause machine learning bias.[62]

Machine learning algorithms will inevitably automate some clinical processes, but researchers and patients need to be aware of their shortcomings and their ability to drive deci-sions that adversely affect protected classes. The risk of letting algorithmic biases go unchecked impacts clinical care, as one widely used algorithm was found to systematically discrim-inate against black people. A study published in *Science* in October 2019 concluded that an algorithm was less likely to refer black people than white people who were equally sick to programs that aim to improve care for patients with complex medical needs.[63] Hospitals and insurers use the algorithm and others like it to help manage care for about two hundred million people in the United States each year.[64]

---

62 Cami Rosso, "The Conundrum of Machine Learning and Cognitive Biases," Medium, accessed on January 10, 2020.

63 Ziad Obermeyer, et al, "Dissecting racial bias in an algorithm used to manage the health of populations." *Science* 336 no. 6464 (2019): 447.

64 Heidi Ledford, "Millions of black people affected by racial bias in health-care algorithms," *Nature Research Journal*, October 26, 2019.

How was this prejudice introduced? Despite the good intentions of the makers of the algorithm, the application was vulnerable to hidden biases due to underlying assumptions made during its development. In this case, the algorithm assigned risk scores to patients on the basis of total health care costs accrued in one year. Higher total costs represent riskier patients with greater health needs. The authors of the study found that since, overall, less money is spent on black patients who have the same level of need, the algorithm falsely concluded that black patients are healthier than equally sick white patients.[65] As a result, black patients were less likely to be referred to health programs that provide more personalized care.[66] If the algorithm were used in research or as a case study, the finding would be alarming on its own, but it was actually used to allocate health care to patients in US hospitals, and hidden biases were found after its implementation. Rather than risk scores based on total health care cost, possibly using greater use of ICD or CPT codes would have led to more accurate measure of health need, since these codes reflect actual treatment.

From a software engineering perspective, teasing out potential biases in machine learning models can be difficult, especially if the model is built with minimal guidance from domain experts and without thorough testing. One researcher and physician, Ziad Obermeyer of UC–Berkeley,

65 Ziad Obermeyer, et al, "Dissecting racial bias in an algorithm used to manage the health of populations." *Science* 336 no. 6464 (2019): 447.

66 Heidi Ledford, "Millions of black people affected by racial bias in health-care algorithms," *Nature Research Journal*, October 26, 2019.

is working with the algorithm's developers to improve the algorithm and address its biases.[67]

ORIGINS OF ETHICS IN MEDICAL RESEARCH

While some of the ethical challenges facing machine learning tools are novel, ethical frameworks that guide clinical decision-making date back several decades. Clues into the desire to use scientific discovery for the benefit of humanity are found centuries ago, in Sir Francis Bacon's *Novum Organum*, which was published in 1620 (and can be found today as an e-book). Medical research ethics, more broadly the field of bioethics, exist to help determine morally right and wrong decisions in healthcare. As healthcare technology becomes more advanced, new ethical questions arise. For example, as use of medical ventilators increased in the 1950s and later, the medical community needed to figure out when it's morally acceptable to turn off a ventilator for someone who might not recover. Given the gene editing capabilities today, what are the ethical boundaries for using gene editing for human enhancement?

Abuses in the medical research community also prompted the need for bioethical frameworks—the Nuremberg trials in 1945 and 1946 identified abominable medical procedures conducted by Nazis on concentration camp victims. Poor, rural, African Americans were abused during the Tuskegee syphilis studies during the 1930s-70s in the unethical effort to understand untreated syphilis.

---

67   Ibid.

Such shameful abuses create distrust between the public and the medical community. From these, and other, abuses emerged several legal and ethical frameworks including the Nuremberg Code (1947), and the National Research Act (1974), which requires institutional review boards (IRBs) to review and oversee research with human subjects. Two notable documents that established ethics foundations are the Declaration of Helsinki (1964) and the Belmont Report (1979), which outline ethical principles for clinical care and biomedical research.

The Declaration of Helsinki has been amended multiple times and was first adopted in 1964 by the World Medical Association—a group conceived during World War II that operates within the World Health Organization. The document outlines three parts: Basic Principles, Medical Research Combined with Clinical Care (Clinical Research), and Non-Therapeutic Biomedical Research Involving Human Subjects (Non-Clinical Biomedical Research). While the declaration makes no mention of machine learning, the underlying principles impact delivery of care irrespective of the tools being used. Two basic principles outlined below have impacts in the field of health care AI.[68]

PRINCIPLE 2:

"The design and performance of each experimental procedure involving human subjects should be clearly formulated in an experimental protocol, which should be transmitted for consideration, comment and guidance to a specially appointed committee independent of the investigator and the sponsor."

---

68   World Medical Association Declaration of Helsinki," June 1964.

PRINCIPLE 5:

"Every biomedical research project involving human subjects should be preceded by careful assessment of predictable risks, in comparison with foreseeable benefits to the subject or to others. Concern for the interests of the subject must always prevail over the interests of science and society."

Designing machine learning tools used to inform clinical decision-making can be thought of as an experiment whose risks need to be carefully evaluated before implementation in clinical practice. Principle 2 alludes to the creation of IRBs and data-related subcouncils of the IRB that evaluate the ethics of proposed research and recommend methods to ensure ethical stewardship of research and clinical data. It also alludes to the creation of HIPAA. Today at some academic medical centers, data scientists assess the likelihood of re-identifying patients and report re-identification risks to data subcouncils.

The Belmont Report also outlines basic ethical principles that underlie the conduct of biomedical and behavioral research involving human subjects; it is the outcome of a four-day period of discussions following the passing of the National Research Act into law in 1974. The basic ethical principles call for respect for persons, beneficence, and justice (i.e., fairness in distribution of medical services and the results of biomedical research).[69] Is it a reasonable

69 "Belmont Report: Ethical Principles and Guidelines for the Protection of Human Subjects of Research," Department of Health, Education, and Warfare, Report of the National Commission for the Protection of Human Subjects of Biomedical and Behavioral Research.

expectation for a computer programmer developing clinical machine learning models to be conversant in the Declaration of Helsinki and the Belmont Report? Probably not. But guiding policies of the institutions and tech companies who develop the tools should be congruent. If groups who develop health care AI tools do not understand HIPAA guidelines and potential ethical violations, their tools probably won't be adopted, and creators of the predictive tools could face significant fines.

Development of health care AI technology carries enormous momentum, and the speed at which development is occurring is introducing ethical challenges. These challenges include how to evaluate algorithm performance and how to determine where such technologies can be safely and efficiently applied to (especially) clinical settings. A few broad examples of ethical issues relate to:

1. Biases in training data.
2. The potential replacing of human health care providers with AI tools.
3. Responding to an AI intervention that has failed. If we develop an AI tool that influences a clinical decision, and a poor decision was made, how do we (as humans) respond?

Inherent to these challenges is the reality that the technology is developing more quickly than our ability to construct ethical frameworks to guide their development. Indeed, much development occurs in the absence of well-defined ethical frameworks specific to health care AI. This reality is not an entirely bad thing since improving the accuracy and speed of health care decisions is a main motivator for development of health care AI tools, but it involves risks, especially if ethical shortcomings are introduced in clinical settings before being vetted within the confines of research.

Stephane Helleringer is a social demography researcher interested in measuring demographic indicators in countries with limited recorded health data. In rural Senegal, Helleringer has begun testing computer vision tools that estimate a subject's age to compensate for birth records and other reliable sources of demographic information that are either missing or destroyed. Reliable and accurate demographic information is the foundation for evidence-based health care and measuring health equity across populations. One of Helleringer's projects focuses on testing new ways to collect demographic data in settings where civil registration systems are incomplete. In rural Senegal, he has developed new AI tools to estimate age from photographs using computer vision, a form of machine learning, and he tested whether the age of an individual can be estimated solely from a photograph of their face.[70] The project takes place in the Niakhar area of Senegal, where detailed birth records haven't been collected since the 1960s.[71]

Helleringer first became interested in machine learning around 2015, when he learned of research projects that

---

70 "Faculty Directory: Stéphane Helleringer, PhD," web page, Johns Hopkins Bloomberg School of Public Health, accessed on August 22, 2019.

71 Global Projects," Johns Hopkins Bloomberg School of Public Health, accessed on November 10, 2019.

inferred age from photographs. He thinks a nascent trend exists in the social sciences toward using new methods, like machine learning, to extract more information from existing data sources, like photographs.

A core challenge to advancing Helleringer's project is finding more training data. Currently, his computer vision models have trained only on photographs from Senegalese women aged eighteen to sixty-five.[72] Therefore, this model might not operate as accurately with non-Senegalese populations. To improve the extensibility of the computer vision model, his team is working at other sites in Africa by photographing people from a broader range of ethnicities. A key question emerged: are his age prediction models extendable to other communities? What the team has learned in Senegal might not be transferable to Ghana, for example, or to countries in East Africa. One of their next steps is conducting experiments to see if they can accurately predict age in Tanzania on the basis of models trained using data from Senegal, which could potentially reveal the suspected bias in their model.

Helleringer and his team are not alone in confronting the challenge of biases or overtraining in machine learning models. Bias is a core issue for any machine learning model and can originate from multiple sources. Helleringer's photoset reflects only a small subset of a larger population. In this case, the narrow scope of the data is rather obvious. Unless the model is later trained on data from broader sources,

---

72 Stéphane Helleringer, "Improving age measurement in low- and middle-income countries through computer vision: A test in Senegal," Vol. 40, Art. 9:(219-26), January 29, 2019.

Helleringer's tool should be limited to estimating the ages of people from the same Senegalese population. And since Helleringer is transparent about the data limitations by describing them in his research paper, anyone who wants to use the computer vision models will know of their limitations and inherent bias.

When additional data sources are used to train the model, however, spotting these limitations becomes more of a challenge. In the commercial space, where software is often proprietary, data limitations are not always transparent, and unknowingly applying a machine learning model in a scenario where its hidden biases will produce an inaccurate result poses a risk to the user. To name a couple common causes, data-related biases can result from class imbalance (i.e., unequal numbers of disease and non-disease examples in a dataset), and from lack of independent test sets (i.e., when data from the same patient exist in the dataset used to create the model and the dataset used to test the model). There are multiple strategies to address biases in training data during the development, and for an in-depth discussion, Coursera's AI for Medical Diagnosis course offers good tutorials.

* * *

Data-related biases are objective, but subjective biases exist too and are more difficult to identify. These biases, pointed out by Cathy O'Neil in *Weapons of Math Destruction*, relate to the motivations behind creation of machine learning tools. As an example outside of health care but illustrative of the same bias challenges in health care, O'Neil describes a machine learning tool used to evaluate teacher performance to show that a model's blind spots reflect the judgments and priorities of its creators who are human.[73] O'Neil points out that administrators in Washington, DC used a predictive tool to evaluate teachers largely on the basis of students' scores while ignoring other potential features, like whether the teacher engages students or whether students come to class with underlying personal and family issues.

To the administrators, a tool solely based on student test scores was sufficient, even though this is not the best or only way to evaluate talent. Ultimately, administrators are concerned about test scores, which are measurable and can be standardized across districts and states. O'Neil, who is wary of misuses of data science, points out that "attempting to reduce human behavior, performance, and potential to algorithms is no easy job."[74] In this case, the model was built to rely heavily on test scores instead of measuring a teacher's abilities and efforts. The model ignored human factors that reflect well on the teachers and also ignored external stressors that affect test scores, such as family relocations. These factors were not included in the predictive model that evaluated performance and ultimately led to a critical hiring decision—whether to retain a teacher or find a new one.

In the case of the model that evaluates teacher performance, administrators face an objective challenge in quantifying the external factors and collecting data on those factors. An administrator can't reliably collect data on how a teenage

---

73 Cathy O'Neil, *Weapons of Math Destruction*. Crown Books Publishing, p. 21, September 2016.

74 Ibid.

student feels about their family's recent move to a new school district. Assuming the student is willing to talk to their guidance counselor about being bullied in the week leading up to their test, the guidance counselor would need to record that interaction in a machine-readable way, such as using checkboxes that are later represented numerically. As suggested by the model that evaluates teacher performance, relevant factors often go uncollected, despite significantly impacting the outcome. In other words, even sophisticated machine learning models sometimes fail to quantify or capture all the factors that influence human behavior.

* * *

Coming back to health care, Helleringer's team realized that bias in age estimates was influenced by other behaviors, such as alcohol or tobacco consumption. While reviewing their models, they realized that they systematically overestimated the age of people who consume alcohol. They also realized that their model for age estimation was biased upward for the youngest age groups since the distribution of their training data favored higher ages. Interestingly, they also acknowledge makeup and ritual scarification as factors that modify facial appearance and could have confounded their age estimates. Helleringer sets a good example in his pilot project by identifying limitations. Teams developing machine learning models need to be transparent about the limitations of their models, which can be culturally sensitive and specific, and also about how their models were tested. It's standard practice for published studies to report on metrics of sensitivity and specificity, although commercial, non-published models that are not subject to peer review can be more opaque.

Collecting data is an essential step in the development of AI tools. While Helleringer's computer vision project represents a significant opportunity to gather demographic data, similar projects must heed the same caution to properly gain consent from human subjects. Many health data are sensitive and personal, and photographs are no exception, especially given their role in the development of government-sponsored surveillance programs, particularly in China.[75] Given the concern toward surveillance programs, San Francisco recently banned use of facial recognition technology by police and city agencies.[76] In medicine, MRI and CT scans must be stripped from identifying information prior to sharing unless the patient consents to their use for research, since the scans could be used to re-identify a patient. Research projects like those led by Helleringer show us how care must be taken to not share the training data (i.e., facial photographs) without consent of the participants and to avoid unauthorized uses of the data. Given the grant-funded nature of the project, the code developed by the team is open-source, meaning anyone can download, evaluate, and edit the code for their own purposes. The possibility exists for other groups to use code such as Helleringer's on their own training datasets. While arguably tedious and nuanced, the development team has the responsibility of properly documenting and communicating known biases produced by their code.

---

75   "In the Age of AI." PBS, accessed on December 2, 2019.

76   Shannon Van Sant and Richard Gonzalez, "San Francisco Approves Ban on Government's Use of Facial Recognition Technology," NPR, accessed on August 17, 2019.

CLINICAL READINESS

Sampling biases are important, but perhaps they're not the most troubling ethical concern when it comes to AI in health care. After the data are collected, their limitations are known, and the accuracy of the model is tested, how do we know whether the model is ready to be used in a clinical setting? How do we know whether the model works well enough to actually be placed in clinical environments that impact real patients?[77] Although a study might use data from a million people, how diverse are the participants? Using the computer vision example from Helleringer, images were collected from a population of 353 women. In any study, collected data should be representative of the entire population being investigated. In the case of Helleringer's model, data are only being used in the narrow role of estimating age, but if someone were to extend the model to a larger population, they would need to consider which groups were left out from the training data. Ethicist I. Glenn Cohen asks the question: If racial and other minorities are left out, how will their exclusion affect the model in ways that might benefit or more likely disfavor the model when it's applied to a subpopulation?[78]

Cohen is faculty director of the Petrie-Flom Center at Harvard Law School, which focuses on matters of health law policy, biotechnology, and bioethics. Cohen focuses on prickly issues at the intersection of medical technology and ethics. According to Cohen, he considers thorny issues to include everything from trying to determine how likely a patient will

---

77 *Harvard Global Health Institute.* "I. Glenn Cohen—AI in Health care: Legal and Ethical Issues," May 23, 2019, video, 11:06.

78 Ibid.

have negative cardiac events, to deciding whether to recommend that a particular patient be prescribed pre-exposure prophylaxis.[79]

As a lawyer and ethicist, Cohen says that he sometimes brings the cloud and sometimes the rain to the table, but that we need to think about the clouds and the rain when building machine learning algorithms for health care.[80] Broadly, Cohen describes three main obstacles inherent in developing and applying machine learning algorithms to health care problems: obtaining the data, sharing the data/ownership, and privacy issues.[81]

OBTAINING THE DATA

As we've explored, the EHR is arguably regarded as the current core source of data for training machine learning models, even though accuracy issues typically exist. No EHR system is perfect, and some estimates suggest that about 75 percent of EHR data are accurate. When using clinical data, such as EHR data for development of machine learning tools, Cohen

79 I. Glenn Cohen, "Ethics & the Law – I. Glenn Cohen, Professor of Law at Harvard University – Technology, Law, Ethics, and What's on the Horizon." August 20, 2019, in *Finding Genius Podcast Future Tech Edition*, produced by Richard Jacobs, podcast, 35:44.

80 *Harvard Global Health Institute.* "I. Glenn Cohen—AI in Health care: Legal and Ethical Issues," May 23, 2019, video, 11:06.

81 Cohen, I. Glenn. "Ethics & the Law – I. Glenn Cohen, Professor of Law at Harvard University – Technology, Law, Ethics, and What's on the Horizon." August 20, 2019, in *Finding Genius Podcast Future Tech Edition*, produced by Richard Jacobs, podcast, 35:44.

asks: Do patients need to be explicitly consented for the use of their clinical data for development of machine learning models?[82] The answer is yes, if those data are HIPAA-protected and contain personally identifiable information. Currently, a significant portion of health AI development is dependent on data that have been collected historically, posing a challenge to obtaining consent for use of the data since collection of the data has already occurred. In some cases, the data were collected years ago. If a researcher wishes to abstract identifiable information or create a limited dataset for research purposes, they can request an IRB waiver of consent to use HIPAA-protected data, if the research involves minimal risk to the privacy of individual patients. Such a waiver does not permit a researcher to contact those patients however.

Practically speaking, how can the researcher track down a patient to ask them if it's okay to use their data in the development of a machine learning model? Cohen offers a few ideas, such as creation of "front door" consent, when services are initiated, or the first time someone goes to the hospital.[83] Such a consent would allow patients to know upfront that their data could be used for development of machine learning tools at a later date. It could serve as an opportunity to let patients opt in to stay informed about the outcomes of how their data are being used.

A relatively small number of research institutions have already developed broad models for consent that permit use of data

---

82 *Harvard Global Health Institute.* "I. Glenn Cohen—AI in Health care: Legal and Ethical Issues," May 23, 2019, video, 11:06.

83 Ibid.

for multiple purposes. For example, models have been developed at Mayo and Vanderbilt, but they are exceptions among a majority of research institutions that have not developed or used broad consents. Broad consent allows the researcher to use an individual's biological sample or data in future research.[84] In many cases, research consents are study-specific, so any research conducted on those data remain specific to the original research protocol and cannot be used for future, unrelated research. Researchers can use de-identified forms of EHR data without consent; this is a common way in which EHR data are currently used for development of machine learning models for research purposes. Today, it's pretty common for patients to not know if de-identified forms of data are being used to develop predictive models, which begs the question: at what point do patients need to become aware that their data are being used to create predictive tools?

Some academic institutions, like Johns Hopkins, are finding ways to share research results with study participants. And, according to Jim Potter, an assistant professor of medicine at Johns Hopkins, "if you want patients to be involved, they need to be partners in the study." Study participants are empowered when they know the outcomes of their study, and they are more willing to participate in the study if it entails an expectation that results will be shared. Potter suggests that study teams inform patients of the results of a study. He points out that the results need to be presented in a way that patients can understand. A typical patient will probably not search PubMed for clinical trial results, as the scientific results

---

84   Mark Sheehan, "Can Broad Consent be Informed Consent?" *Public Health Ethics* 4, no. 3 (2011): 226.

shared within PubMed are not always easily understood by the public, and most academic journal articles are restricted behind paywalls. While academic researchers have a good understanding of accuracy metrics used in machine learning models and can communicate those results among themselves, the general public typically doesn't have a good understanding of ROC curves, precision, recall, and how these metrics relate to the study they (or their data) were involved in. Providing clinical trials results to patients builds trust between patients and providers. Offering understandable interpretations to the patient is critical to establishing a healthy long-term relationship between study teams and research participants.

Once an individual consents to research, researchers can begin to collect and analyze the data. At Johns Hopkins, analytical tools like TriNetX are used to query across 1.5 million Hopkins patients in real time within a matter of seconds and return de-identified statistics to the person running the query. Additional approvals are needed if the researcher wants to actually re-identify patients. Use of tools like TriNetX are closely governed by the university, and if a Hopkins researcher wants to retrieve patient-identifiable data from a TriNetX query, they need to receive IRB approval. Once the researcher receives IRB approval, the IRB requests that data management of the PHI is reviewed by the research data subcouncil of the Data Trust, which is a governance board that evaluates the purpose and motivations of querying patients' identifiable data.

SHARING THE DATA

Academic medical centers have a responsibility as stewards of patient data to use the data only for agreed-upon uses, and sharing patient data, even de-identified data, is highly cautioned and restricted in academic circles. If shared incorrectly, huge financial penalties can result for the provider, and patient trust (and potentially their identity) is compromised. At many large academic medical centers, only de-identified data can be shared with industry partners, while identifiable patient data remains stored behind institutional firewalls. Business use agreements and business associate agreements govern the sharing of de-identified data to outside collaborators.

TriNetX, as one example, has partnered with multiple academic research centers to optimize discovery of patients for clinical trials, among other applications. A large academic medical center like Johns Hopkins has hundreds of ongoing clinical trials at any given time and, as a member of the TriNetX network, could potentially share de-identified patient data with TriNetX and other large institutions to determine if enough patients could qualify for a clinical trial; knowing the number of patients who meet inclusion and exclusion criteria helps the researcher determine eligibility for clinical trials and for potential NIH funding opportunities. Sharing patient data, even de-identified data, is not straightforward, but the ability to do so could enable users of TriNetX or similar platforms to query relevant clinical trials' data across EHRs representing millions of patients.

Agreeing to share their data with a larger network, like TriNetX, will allow hospitals to query across larger populations of patients and fuel discoveries by establishing more comprehensive training sets. Sharing data with a third party is tricky, however, since universities and hospitals have a responsibility to honor the initial consents signed by patients. The case for broad consents becomes stronger from the perspective of developing machine learning models. If patients agree to future use of their data for multitudes of studies, large academic research centers can more easily share data among each other and use the data for multiple studies and to develop predictive models. At Johns Hopkins, de-identified data can be shared under appropriate agreements, and the data being shared need to go through honest brokers. There are good reasons for this practice since regional medical centers may be re-identified based on numerous possible adverse events. For example, if an institution performs a rare or risky procedure with high fatality rate, that institution (and potentially its patients) could be re-identified among its peers.

RELIGION AND AI

In February 2020, IBM and Microsoft joined with the Vatican to sign an ethical resolution: the "Rome Call for AI Ethics," which aims to serves as a set of guidelines for developing artificial intelligence in a way that preserves human rights. The pledge was presented to Pope Francis by Microsoft, IBM, Vatican officials, and the Chinese director-general of the UN Food and Agriculture Organization.[85] "The Rome Call for AI Ethics" establishes the expectation that AI must show "not only how AI algorithms come to their decisions but also what their purpose and objectives are."[86] One could wonder: how

85   Javier Espinoza, "IBM and Microsoft sign Vatican Pledge for Ethical AI," Financial Times, accessed on March 3, 2020.

86   Ibid.

does this differ from robust, transparent software development practices?

Francesca Rossi, IBM's global AI ethics leader, points out how The Vatican is not an expert on the technology, rather on values, he and describes the collaboration as a way to aid the Vatican and society in understanding how to use AI with those values.[87] Some of the hesitations people feel toward AI are addressed in the pledge by vowing to respect privacy and work without bias. However, it remains to be seen if and how the pledge would be enforced—what good is a pledge without consequences when a violation occurs? By focusing on increasing awareness among companies and entities that implement AI, the pledge sets out to safeguard human rights in an effort to "humanize technology and not 'technologize' humanity."[88]

The idea for this initiative started with remarks Pope Francis gave at a Vatican technology conference in 2019 attended by executives from Facebook, Mozilla, and Western Digital, as well as Catholic ethicists, government regulators, internet entrepreneurs, and venture capitalists.[89] He said technology needs theoretical and moral principles, and how use of AI has implications in all areas of human activity, including political interference, the spreading of false information,

---

87 Ibid.

88 Christine Fisher, "IBM and Microsoft Support the Vatican's Guidelines for Ethical AI," MSN, accessed on March 31, 2020.

89 Philip Pullella, "Pope Urges Silicon Valley to Avoid Slide Toward New 'Barbarism,'" Reuters, accessed on October 1, 2019.

and the ability to promote a form of law by the strongest if unchecked.[90]

The pope recognized that the misuse of AI would have detrimental effects on political and social tensions given just how much the application of AI could hold implications in every aspect of human activity. His remarks reflect the real and credible threat that artificial intelligence can pose to mankind if misused—whether intentionally (the deliberate spread of political propaganda to incite fear or anxiety among a populace) or unintentionally (such as the racial biases introduced at the beginning of the chapter).

The fact that some technology companies are turning toward organized religion to instill human and ethical values into technology development is an interesting dynamic. As the development and testing of machine learning tools become more transparent, will a patient wonder if their diagnosis was informed by Catholic values? For someone who does not identify with Catholicism, would that person question or potentially refuse the treatment or ask for a second opinion? Could use of religious doctrine become a branding of sorts, where one model is informed by principles of the Vatican while another model is informed by the Koran or by Buddhist thought? Will a basic, mutual understanding of the differences between the values of world religions become more important for progress toward the common good?

To be sure, a good amount of speculation is happening here, and some agreement over human values is probably needed

---

90 Ibid.

if religion informs technology development in health care. Potential problems could arise if "not shared" ethical values are applied to thorny issues in decision making in health-care, such as those of euthanasia, reproductive health, and abortion. The discussion of the potential role of religion in AI will likely need to continue to evolve. As is, most patients are not overly concerned with the mechanisms by which their health care tools work, but perhaps a factor as personal as religion will spur discussion and involvement, and religion could emerge as a factor that is included by explainable AI.

CHAPTER 5:

REGULATORY AND LEGAL CONSIDERATIONS

All orgs developing advanced AI should be regulated, including Tesla.

—ELON MUSK, ENTREPRENEUR, INVESTOR, AND CEO OF TESLA AND SPACEX[91]

In July 2019, the Lancet HIV journal published research that used electronic health record data and machine learning to predict whether a particular man was at high risk of contracting HIV, thus enabling his physician to determine whether to put him on pre-exposure prophylaxis (PrEP).[92] Should a physician, whose clinical decision to recommend PrEP is at least partially influenced by the result of the machine learning tool, need to disclose to the patient that machine learning was used? Is the machine learning tool akin to some knowledge base, like a journal article or clinical grand rounds talk,

---

91 Elon Musk, Twitter Post. February 17, 2020, 6:22 PM.

92 Julia Marcus, et al, "Use of Electronic Health Record Data and Machine Learning to Identify Candidates for HIV Pre-exposure Prophylaxis: A Modelling Study," *The Lancet HIV.* July 5, 2019.

or to expert opinion, like another physician, or is the tool something else entirely?

A lot of the legal issues and frameworks have centered on data-sharing and whether patient privacy rights have been upheld under current legal protection, namely HIPAA, when machine learning tools are developed using patient data. The legal discussion surrounding machine learning tools is becoming more complex as machine learning tools gain more autonomy and more "personhood." Discussions are just now emerging on stable frameworks for informed consent and how to facilitate informed consent for situations where machine learning models are influencing clinical decisions.

Legal and regulatory factors have governed data-sharing and use within health care, and the emergence of AI has introduced new definitions of health care data that do not fall under the umbrella of traditional protections established by HIPAA. Out of the current necessity of data generators (i.e., hospitals) to partner with experts in developing the technology (i.e., tech companies), health data are being shared, which data-sharing practices need to facilitate in legally appropriate ways. We should note that we are at the dawn of using machine learning in health care, especially for clinical uses. Are there lessons learned that we should retain for future use ten years from now when implementations of machine learning in clinical care are more pervasive?

* * *

Nothing is inherently illegal about AI, yet we face legal challenges in implementing health care AI tools that use traditional, HIPAA-protected patient data. The use of patient data is key. Anyone can install the necessary programming tools on their computer, download publicly available de-identified health data, and begin to create machine learning models for research's sake. Many government agencies and programs, including CMS and Medicare, make de-identified data publicly available on their websites.[93,94] Publicly available datasets also exist for studying genomics. Again, for research, one can find nearly endless (and growing) sources of public health and medical data that can serve as training data for machine learning models.

Publicly available datasets are excellent resources for creating hypotheses, for initial exploration, and for brainstorming. Creating a simple machine learning model is relatively easy, but understanding the context of the data requires subject matter expertise. Also, implementing machine learning tools in clinical settings is subject to health regulations. For example: hospitals outsource some of their diagnostic tests to outside lab test vendors. While each vendor provides the same diagnostic test service (such as evaluating livery chemistry by measuring levels of alanine aminotransferase in serum or plasma samples), reporting levels may be consistently elevated or subdued compared to peer vendors.

---

93   CMS Data, Centers for Medicare and Medicaid Services, accessed on September 29, 2019.

94   Alex Pearlman, "HIPAA Is the Tip of the Iceberg When It Comes to Privacy and Your Medical Data," Harvard Law Petrie-Flom Center, accessed on July 29, 2019.

A keen physician who has ordered and interpreted lab tests knows the nuances of testing among lab test vendors. The physician also knows that proper handling and processing of the blood specimen affects the purity of serum or plasma delivered to the vendor for testing. Such nuances are extremely difficult to decipher on aggregated data (e.g., imagine a training dataset of thousands or millions of patients). Domain knowledge and experience are needed to identify the nuances on the individual level and potentially in aggregate. Implementing machine learning tools that use clinical data and that impact clinical decisions is regulated by frameworks that were established decades ago. HIPAA, the Health Portability and Accountability Act, which defines which health information is protected in the United States, was introduced in 1996.

Building sustainable and robust health care AI tools with lab data requires durable legal frameworks from business and ethics perspectives. Health care data come in many shapes and sizes, and the different types can be categorized in terms of HIPAA. In the following image adapted from I. Glenn Cohen of Harvard's Petrie-Flom Center, we can see more health care data are *not* covered by HIPAA (i.e., "alternative" health data) than covered by the act. Cohen predicts that in the future, most of the inferences we make about people's health and about their lives will be generated with the data below the HIPAA boundary.[95] From a legal perspective, this prediction is pretty incredible and strengthens the argument that HIPAA is becoming outdated.

---

95 *Harvard Global Health Institute.* "I. Glenn Cohen—AI in Health care: Legal and Ethical Issues," May 23, 2019, video, 11:06.

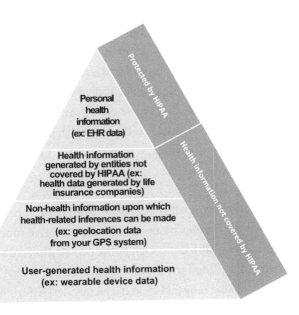

Figure 5.1: HIPAA and non-HIPAA data.[96] The volume of health data not protected by HIPAA data greatly exceeds HIPAA-protected data, and are becoming increasingly relevant for development of predictive tools in health care.[97,98]

The examples of data that fall below the HIPAA boundary today include personal exercise data, social media data, pharmacy or even masseuse data, and geolocation data. Interactive exercise equipment, such as Fitbit and Peloton, logs data for users during workouts, which can later become relevant

---

96 Nicholson Price and I. Glenn Cohen, "Privacy in the age of medical big data," Nature Medicine 27 (2019): 37-43.

97 Ibid.

98 Alex Pearlman, "HIPAA Is the Tip of the Iceberg When It Comes to Privacy and Your Medical Data," Harvard Law Petrie-Flom Center, accessed on July 29, 2019.

for predictive models. By agreeing to use the GPS app on your phone, for example, the maker of that app collects usage data, including the restaurants visited, trips to liquor stores, and trips to the gym. While geolocation data alone probably will not tell a complete story of someone's overall health, someone with access to those data could include the frequency of trips to fast-food restaurants as a feature in a tool that predicts cardiovascular disease.

If a health insurer has access to those data, it is not breaking any legal rules by creating the predictive model using alternative health data, such as the geolocation data showing frequent fast-food trips. Can you spot any potential biases in a model using only fast-food frequency derived from geolocation? What if the person who frequents fast-food restaurants only orders a black coffee? What if that person also frequents the local gym and doesn't use their GPS to travel to the gym?

Today, while all the items displayed in Figure 5.1 are health data, most of us typically don't think of non-traditional sources of health data, which are comprise a significant portion of the lower part of the pyramid. User-generated data, such as the use of a blood-sugar-tracking smartphone app or Google searches about particular symptoms and insurance coverage for serious disorders are not covered by HIPAA.[99] So, according to Cohen, we have to think seriously, whether we only want to protect the data covered by HIPAA line and ignore everything else (i.e., the tip of the pyramid).[100]

---

99 Ibid.

100 *Harvard Global Health Institute.* "I. Glenn Cohen—AI in Health care: Legal and Ethical Issues," May 23, 2019, video, 11:06.

At least outside of clinical settings, the data sitting near the bottom of the pyramid represents a growing majority of the data being used by, and for the development of, health care AI applications.

* * *

So why does HIPAA matter? Why do health data deserve to be protected? And what are health data? HIPAA acts as a legal safeguard against unauthorized disclosure and use of health information; it was passed into law in 1996 with the dual goals of making health care delivery more efficient and increasing the number of Americans with health insurance coverage.[101,102] After becoming law in 1996, HIPAA has undergone amendments, notably in the 2009 HITECH (Health Information Technology for Economic and Clinical Health) Act, which aimed to address challenges arising from electronic health records.[103] After all, when HIPAA was first passed, electronic health records did not exist, and secure transmission of health data was accomplished primarily by fax machine. In an interview, the FDA's acting chief information officer, Amy Abernethy, described how in even earlier

---

101 I. Glenn Cohen, Michelle Mello, "HIPAA and Protecting Health Information in the 21st Century," The Petrie-Flom Center for Health Law Policy, Biotechnology, and Bioethics at Harvard Law School, May 24, 2018.

102 "Beyond the HIPAA Privacy Rule: Enhancing Privacy, Improving Health Through Research," National Center for Biotechnology Information, US National Library of Medicine, 2009.

103 I. Glenn Cohen, Michelle Mello, "HIPAA and Protecting Health Information in the 21st Century," JAMA Network, July 17, 2018.

times, the FDA would receive paper applications by the truck load and by horse and buggy![104] Secure data transfer has come a long way since then.

In 1996, health data were concentrated in health insurance companies and on paper records in your doctor's office and pharmacy. As those health data became digital, HIPAA needed to adapt accordingly. Of course, insurance companies have always been a stakeholder in health information, but new nontraditional stakeholders emerged. Banks and social media have also started to collect and analyze health data. And with consolidation among the makers of popular consumer applications, such as Google and Waze, companies are able to increase their stake in health care through mergers and acquisitions. A danger emerges when financial interests conflict with the clinical interests of the patient. Pictures and narratives describing personal health conditions posted on social media could be sold or transferred to third parties, such as an insurance company or financial institution, without knowledge of the user. Without legal protection, an insurance company could use that information to inform a decision about coverage or premiums without violating HIPAA. Doing so would probably come as a surprise to the patient, if the patient were to ever find out.

Ultimately, the development of health AI tools is dependent on the availability of patient data, even if de-identified. An initiative announced in 2018 by the Trump administration, MyHealthEData, ensures that patients can control their health data

---

104 Amy Abernethy, Vijay Pand, "Food, Drugs, and Tech—100 Years of Public Health," Andreessen Horowitz, accessed on January 20, 2020.

and decide how it is going to be used.[105] Accordingly to Cohen, MyHealthEData is part of a larger movement to make greater use of patient data to improve care and health; it seeks to make information available wherever patients receive care and to allow patients to share information with apps and other online services that may help them manage their care.[106] Data relevant to MyHealthEData will include the data at the tip of the pyramid in Figure 5.1, such as each patient's electronic health record. The initiative will not affect more non-traditional forms of health data, which are much harder to govern yet growing more important in the development of health care AI tools.

SOFTWARE AS A MEDICAL DEVICE (SAMD)

In this book and in common vernacular, machine learning technology that affects health care is collectively referred to as AI tools. From a regulatory standpoint, what does that mean? The FDA has approved or cleared AI/ML-based software as a medical device, calling it "SaMD," which is software that is on its own a medical device and not part of a hardware medical device[107]—with "locked" algorithms.[108] The FDA defines a

---

105 "Trump Administration Announces MyHealthEData Initiative at HIMSS18," US Centers for Medicare and Medicaid Services, accessed on August 13, 2019.

106 I. Glenn Cohen, Michelle Mello, "HIPAA and Protecting Health Information in the 21st Century," JAMA Network, July 17, 2018.

107 "Software as a medical device (SaMD)," US Food and Drug Administration (FDA), accessed on January 24, 2020.

108 "Proposed regulatory framework for modifications to artificial intelligence/ machine learning (AI/ML)-based software as a medical device (SaMD)," Food & Drug Administration. 2019.

locked algorithm as one "that provides the same result each time the same input is applied to it and does not change without use."[109] Since many algorithms adapt to their inputs, the FDA is changing its approach to evaluating AI/ML tools in medicine and has proposed a "total product lifecycle (TPLC) regulatory approach" that permits continuous improvement of these tools while maintaining their safety and effectiveness.[110]

How will this new approach impact the machine learning engineer? The answer is unclear, but to comply with FDA guidelines and potential audits, reproducibility of machine learning models under various conditions will probably be enforced (and should be included in good programming practices).

ALTERNATIVE DATA: CHALLENGES

These alternative forms of health data—those not found in the EHR system or at the office of a designated health care provider—present technical opportunities and legal challenges. To what degree do these data need to be protected by law? Can these data be reasonably de-identified? Assuming people know they are generating alternative health data, how would a user consent to generation and sharing of the data? The reality is that a lot of the alternative health data will be generated by applications on mobile devices—phones, wearable health devices, watches—and consent to data generation is somewhat de facto through their use. Currently,

---

109 Ibid.

110 "Software as a medical device (SaMD)," US Food and Drug Administration (FDA), 2018, accessed on January 24, 2020.

data collection and disclosure forms are available, but the reality is that these forms are lengthy and seldom read by the user. In a familiar scene, the user will rapidly scroll through a lengthy Terms and Conditions page and quickly agree in order to use a mobile application. What would a more effective data agreement policy look like?

Patients do not want to be surprised at the potential unauthorized use of their health data. In 2017, Google partnered with the University of Chicago Medical Center to use patient data from electronic health records for development of AI tools to improve diagnosis. In June 2019, Google and the University of Chicago were sued in a potential class-action lawsuit accusing the hospital of sharing hundreds of thousands of patients' records with Google without removing identifiable date stamps or doctor's notes.[111] The lawsuit underscores the need to comply with HIPAA regulations and to receive express consent from patients to disclose medical records to industry partners.[112] In this case, it's claimed that Google failed to remove personal information such as individuals' height, weight, and vital signs, whether they suffer from specific diseases like cancer or AIDS, and records of recent medical procedures, such as transplants and abortions.[113] By themselves, these factors are not PHI, but when

---

111 Daisuke Wakabayashi, "Google and the University of Chicago Are Sued Over Data Sharing," New York Times, June 26, 2019, accessed on August 18, 2019.

112 Ibid.

113 James Vincent, "Google accused of inappropriate access to medical data in potential class-action lawsuit," The Verge, accessed on November 2, 2019.

combined with time stamps, individuals could potentially be re-identified.

A more indirect example comes from Target's use of purchase history to identify a pregnant teenager before her parents found out. Around 2012, customers began discovering that Target analyzed purchase data by connecting the purchase credit card number to demographic information available within Target or elsewhere. Statisticians at Target were about to identify about twenty-five products that, when analyzed together, allowed the statisticians to assign the shopper a "pregnancy prediction" score and even estimate the trimester of pregnancy depending on the products purchased.[114] As a result, Target sent baby-related coupons to the home of a pregnant teenager. Her father saw the coupons and contacted Target in anger, thinking the company was encouraging his daughter to become pregnant. He later found out she was already pregnant and Target had used her purchase history to predict her pregnancy.

Research physician Dr. Kamal Maheshwari, who directs the Center for Perioperative Intelligence and is a practicing anesthesiologist at the Cleveland Clinic, asks: what is the best way to protect patients while avoiding overprotection that stifles collaboration and well-intentioned development of AI tools? Maheshwari believes widespread agreement exists that health data can help improve patient care, but the data are personal and prone to misuse. Therefore, we should reasonably be cautious about the use of health data beyond clinical care and

---

114 Kashmir Hill, "How Target Figured Out a Teen Girl Was Pregnant before Her Father Did," Forbes, accessed on September 3, 2019.

the purpose should be clear. However, the overabundance of caution often manifests itself as a lack of trust from the patient and a fear of litigation from the provider. The patient becomes fearful of misuse of data and may resist or resent granting consent to use their data. The provider becomes fearful of being sued for a lack of oversight, mistake or data leak. This adversarial climate stifles innovation in academic settings where innovation should be at the epicenter. Furthermore, it's unclear who (hospitals or government or industry) should make the initial needed investment in making health data safe and useful.

Specific to the development of AI tools, Maheshwari has observed a lack of patient involvement with the development of machine learning tools. Without adequate patient involvement, it's hard for the patient to learn of the outcome of research and also leads to a gray area of data ownership. The patient wonders: *Were my data actually useful to the study? Did the study benefit other patients?* Related to data ownership, many patients are interested in retaining copies of their health data for personal use and for sharing with providers during major changes, such as employment, since employment is still closely tied to health insurance. As a hopeful exception to this trend, good progress is being made to increase patient awareness of research results at places like Cleveland Clinic and Johns Hopkins. Maheshwari suggests that patients should be educated about the potential benefit of health data sharing and how development of AI tools could benefit them and society at large. Many researchers believe patients should be entitled to receive a copy of their data or the information generated with the help of their data. Doing so aligns with Jim Potter's encouragement of clinical research teams partnering with their patients. Note that patients do not always understand the intricacies of their own health data, especially complex labs and genetic tests, which poses a risk of misinterpretation if sharing of health data is not closely coupled with education about procedures and results.

SOME POSSIBLE SOLUTIONS

Academic medical centers have a responsibility to safeguard their data, yet the most successful models will allow for a three-way partnership between academic medical centers, industry, and patients. Currently, we can observe mixed incentives. How does the legal field address the misaligned incentives of medical centers safeguarding detailed patient data and the desire for industry to use health data to develop an app that provides benefit to the patient but also generates financial profit? Medical centers want to gather as much data as possible to provide good care for their patients and also to conduct research studies. Ideally, they want to limit access of sensitive data to only their own researchers but also partner with patients. Industry wants to access data for building new tools, which companies intend to sell for profit. Most patients just want to protect their privacy from systems that could treat them as resources to be exploited.

Yoky Matsuoka, who has led projects at Google Health and is known for her contributions to robotics in health care, has hinted at some of the ways patients might become more accepting of sharing their data. In an interview, Matsuoka used Google Maps as an analogy for how users can be initially apprehensive about sharing data with a commercially owned entity but later increasingly use the technology since its value is clear and significant.[115]

In using Google Maps, the user volunteers their location data and probably other data to Google, which then analyzes the data and returns directions and locations in an easy-to-understand way. Similarly, Matsuoka believes that, for people to be willing to share their health data with large platforms like Google, developers of analytics tools need to provide value, and that at the end of the day a little bit of data sharing in a safe way might be okay.[116]

---

115 Lori Sherer, "Yoky Matsuoka of Google Health on the Future of Healthcare," Bain and Company, accessed on July 6, 2019.

116 Ibid.

CHAPTER 6:

INFRASTRUCTURE

———

Having a technical cofounder is absolutely essential because it's fine to have an understanding of user needs, but not understanding what the technology can actually do is highly limiting.

—DAPHNE KOLLER, CEO AND FOUNDER OF INSITRO AND COFOUNDER OF COURSERA[117]

Daphne Koller works at the intersection of machine learning and biology and health as founder of insitro, a drug discovery and development company that uses and designs machine learning algorithms to accelerate drug discovery. Koller described insitro and the structure of the company in an interview at the 2020 Women in Data Science conference. The staff of insitro is split between scientists, many of whom produce the data for the purpose of creating machine learning models, and machine learning engineers, who interpret the data. In a later chapter, we will learn some of the specific ways machine learning is applied to drug discovery and how machine learning can help develop and reveal hypotheses.

117　*SiliconANGLE theCUBE.* "Stanford Women in Data Science (WiDS) Conference 2020."

Koller describes the need for a technical founder to keep the scientific mind in check by defining what is technically possible to build.

Artificial intelligence projects require a supportive research climate to thrive and develop. Health care AI developers rely on a combination of software tools, scientific expertise, various forms of funding and legal frameworks to construct and test their complex models. Although some of the physical lab tools would have been easy to find even a decade ago, many of the software tools have been developed only within the past couple years. Powerful new algorithms and hardware have been developed in other fields of study, and the benefits have transferred to medical research. The rapid pace of change requires researchers to stay current with changing trends in software. Aside from attending to the scientific problems under study, researchers also have to navigate funding programs and stay mindful of ethical issues related to their projects.

At Johns Hopkins, I learned from Jim Potter that software tools always change; rather than focus on a specific programming language, like Python, or collaborative tools like Git or Jupyter notebooks, focus on the necessity of those tools in the first place. Git emerged from a need to share and review code in real time. Jupyter notebooks emerged from the desire to execute code interactively in a portable format akin to a digital notebook. Today, while Jupyter notebooks might be a great tool to use for ideation and peer review of machine learning models and for initial exploring of large datasets, new tools will probably emerge or build upon existing tools in the next few years.

HISTORY, EFFICIENCY, HARDWARE

Back in the 1980s, a powerful and expensive personal computer had only about 128 kilobytes of RAM, and processor speeds were dwarfed compared to even outdated cell phones of today. A used iPhone 5s operating on one gigabyte of RAM can be bought on eBay for under $100. Both the processor and RAM (local memory) are main factors that allow computers and phones to run quickly.

Well-written computer code today needs to be efficient, meaning the calculations performed by the code should use as little of the computer's memory as possible. When memory fills up, the computer starts to run slowly and can freeze up. Since personal computers of the 1980s had no hard drives, computer programs were written on floppy disks. A computer program written by Potter required eighteen single-sided floppy disks and had to be written in machine-readable code, rather than a compiled language, which resides in the computer's memory. (Today, as computer programming languages have modernized, easier-to-use compiled languages like Python are popular, even though they can be computationally bulky. In many cases, but not always, programmers can get away with using somewhat bulkier but friendly languages like Python due to vast improvements in processing power.) In the 1980s, a forty-megabyte server cost about $45,000. Keep in mind that "small" datasets used for machine learning today are in the single megabyte range while complex datasets including the dense images used for digital pathology easily extend into the gigabytes and terabytes.

While infrastructure supporting machine learning in health care requires technical items like servers and programming languages, history has shown that these tools will change.[118] In addition to technical tools, research relies on the following frameworks to support development of robust machine learning models: administrative, training, ethical/legal. Like the technical resources, these frameworks have also changed over time.

ADMINISTRATIVE ITEMS AND FUNDING

Health care administration has come to mean the personnel and processes related to the scheduling and billing of medical services. These processes are essential, and health care could not be delivered at its current level without them. Furthermore, the human component of health care shouldn't be undervalued. As pointed out earlier, these processes are also in the spotlight as an area of overspending and overcomplexity in the US health care system. In terms of implementing machine learning tools supporting health care, some of the same functions exist, but administrative items take on new meaning too.

Given the multiple ways AI tools can be deployed, users include patients, physicians, and even chemists. Any one of these users can adopt and implement machine learning tools in a research setting. To oversimplify, all someone has to do is open their computer, use a programming language like R or Python, download a subset of data, and start building a model. This process might be easier for some people than others, based on their technical training, but doing

118 "Machine learning: what it is and why it matters," SAS, accessed on March 31, 2020.

research in a silo and untethered from clinical restrictions is pretty straightforward.

SOME FUNDING MECHANISMS

In academia, administration supports the grants and hiring needed for developing and deploying machine learning models. The National Institutes of Health (NIH) are a major source of grants supporting machine learning projects for academia, as illustrated by the drug repurposing efforts of Dr. Bryan Roth of UNC-Chapel Hill and others. Grant funding, sometimes from private sources and foundations, provides financial support for startups. For example, macro-eyes is a recipient of Grand Challenges Explorations funding from the Bill & Melinda Gates Foundation and an alumnus of competitive digital health accelerators Dreamit Health and Mass Challenge.

In terms of federal grant funds, opportunities are available depending on the size of the company. The US Small Business Administration (SBA) offers multiple vehicles for funding.[119] Foundations and accelerator programs are sources of private funding. College students can apply for venture funding and participate in startup competitions. Opportunities for students range from the competitive Y Combinator to student-led (and highly selective) venture groups like A-Level Capital to participation in health care hackathons like MedHacks and MIT Hacking Medicine, all of which

---

119 "Small Business Innovation Research (SBIR)," Small Business Administration, accessed on July 9, 2019.

give students valuable exposure to mentors and potential funding sources.[120,121,122,123]

If you are developing machine learning models, who actually applies to these programs? For small companies, the onus typically falls on the founder, which I learned firsthand as a member of consulting firm SoKat. I attended local conferences, met fellow entrepreneurs in the consulting space, and learned about the SBA. I talked with friends with experience in federal consulting and learned of approaches like the Shipley method—an established framework for systematically identifying and responding to federal grant proposals.[124] Without a track record, a small company may have difficulty securing funds, but funding a small company with grants sidesteps the need to seek external funding from investors and to negotiate equity positions.

In any event, funding and administering machine learning projects are only successful if the technology has a well-defined problem to solve, and if the group seeking funds and carrying out the work has a balance of technical and domain expertise.

---

120 Y Combinator, accessed on July 11, 2019.

121 "About Us: MedHacks 2020," MedHacks 2020, accessed on March 31, 2020.

122 "MIT Hacking Medicine,"MIT Hacking Medicine, accessed on March 31, 2020.

123 "A-Level Capital," accessed on March 31, 2020.

124 Shipley Wins, accessed on July 25, 2019.

TRAINING

Over the past few years, the number of good resources available to learn how to code machine learning models has exploded. Coursera, cofounded by Daphne Koller and Andrew Ng, is one excellent example. This development is great for the field, and instructors like Josh Gordon of Google, Andrew Ng of Stanford, and Jim Liew of Johns Hopkins are among the individuals who make the field more accessible. At the same time, physicians like Dr. Robert Miller of Johns Hopkins express well-founded caution about people whose main training is in non-computer-science fields developing machine learning tools with incomplete knowledge of how the models work. Koller adds that people can find many different avenues to enter the fields of data science and machine learning, ranging from the more traditional route of computer science and mathematics to less traditional routes like biology.

Machine learning models, like their human designers, are not infallible. They cannot replicate every nuance of the real-world systems they mirror and are subject to bias. An unavoidable concern is the reality that the people who design these models are susceptible to their own biases and incomplete knowledge. Miller emphasizes that a fair number of people in pathology lack understanding of the math that powers machine learning models for automated pathology diagnosis.

The risk is that someone unfamiliar with the underlying mechanics of the model will apply a "black-box" algorithm to clinical datasets, imparting an unknown bias. Using a machine learning model with an incomplete understanding of its mechanics could lead one to make errors and ultimately engender mistrust. In order for the field of health care AI to prosper, we need more people with combined domain (medical) expertise and data science expertise, who understand the mechanics of machine learning algorithms and the medical problem. Good examples of this partnership can be seen in the outbreak of the 2019 novel coronavirus, COVID-19. Researchers at Johns Hopkins University created an interactive map showing the spread of COVID-19, including confirmed cases, total deaths, and total recovered, drawing from publicly available databases at the CDC, WHO, and local media reports. And in parts of Europe where emergency call centers are overwhelmed with questions about suspected COVID-19 symptoms, researchers are developing AI bots to triage calls.

As Koller alludes to, the intersection of data science and medical disciplines is relatively new, which means we must never rely blindly on these algorithms, and expert human judgment will always be essential. In other words, we can't stop teaching long division just because we have calculators. Dr. Kamal Maheshwari, an anesthesiologist at Cleveland Clinic, sees a similar need for machine learning practitioners who are fluent in both the medical domain and in machine learning. Maheshwari points out that since technical expertise rarely interfaces directly with the caregiver, there is value in someone who can provide care and also knows how to develop the technical, machine learning solutions. Maheshwari does not want to spend time away from his core competency, clinical care, and thus needs experts whose core technical expertise can help develop useful patient care solutions. This logical relationship is not, however, very common within health care, and it represents a divide. The technical expert often does not have expertise or vernacular in clinical matters while the clinical expert often does not know how to write code. The challenge then becomes one of communication and determining how to mesh the two disciplines. According to Maheshwari, there is a need for collaboration between technical and clinical experts and/or development of coding talent who understand the basics of clinical care.

So what does it mean to be fluent in machine learning? And what level of machine learning competency is sufficient to build and evaluate the models? As the examples of Miller and Maheshwari illustrate, the physician is probably not the right person to evaluate the accuracy of machine learning models without training. The risk is deploying black-box models that neither the patient nor the physician understands or is allowed to question or challenge. Without the input and guidance of a domain expert like Miller or Maheshwari, one risks deploying a machine learning model with embedded problems that cannot be easily uncovered.

Physician and health care AI expert Eric Topol points out that, in some cases, we already accept black boxes in medicine. In his luminary book *Deep Medicine*, Topol uses the example of electroconvulsive therapy as a highly effective treatment for severe depression, yet the mechanics of the treatment are not well understood. Topol adds that many drugs seem to work even though no one can explain how. Finally, Topol acknowledges that patients are willing to accept some black boxes in medicine, as long as they make us feel better or improve our condition, but should we do the same for treatments driven by AI algorithms? [125]

---

125 Eric Topol, *Deep Medicine: How Artificial Intelligence Can Make Healthcare Human Again*, New York: Basic Books, 2019.

* * *

My exposure to machine learning began with online tutorials from Codecademy and DataCamp. After learning fundamental programming in Python, I sought ways to use Python to explore and catalog biospecimen datasets. In my spare time, I used Python to analyze financial data and test simple investment strategies. While I can't claim expertise in Python or machine learning programming, my entry into data science and machine learning is not atypical. Bootcamps and online programs exist to train individuals how to write computer programs that perform statistical analysis and how to construct machine learning models using large datasets.

Years later, when I was managing exceptional undergraduate computer science students, the value of a traditional and rigorous computer science training became clear to me. Students and graduates of traditional programs wrote good code much more quickly than I could.

We can also see individuals who had initially followed a traditional path of formal computer science education but changed direction due to a burning desire to build websites and businesses on their own. Greg Brockman and Patrick Collison are good examples. These individuals exemplify the value of actually building things, rather than simply studying the material.

Greg Brockman, cofounder of OpenAI, transitioned into machine learning in a circuitous way. During a gap year after high school, Brockman began programming seriously before enrolling at Harvard, transferring to MIT, and dropping out early to join Patrick Collison to build Stripe, which at that time was a small startup and has since grown to over five hundred employees with a valuation of around $35 billion.

ETHICAL AND LEGAL

Any machine learning project in health care is subject to ethical issues—regardless of whether the project is supported by academia or industry. And since technical development occurs quicker than responses to ethical dilemmas, developing machine learning models with the guidance of a flexible framework, rather than reacting to ethical dilemmas once they occur, would be preferable. Development under an ethical framework would be a more proactive approach.

Google has developed sets of ethical principles for AI applications, not just for health care, but broadly applicable to any domain:[126]

1. Be socially beneficial.
2. Avoid creating or reinforcing unfair bias.
3. Be built and tested for safety.
4. Be accountable to people.
5. Incorporate privacy design principles.
6. Uphold high standards of scientific excellence.
7. Be made available for uses that accord with these principles.

126 "Artificial Intelligence at Google: Our Principles," GoogleAI, accessed on March 31, 2020.

All of these principles make sense when viewed through the lens of health care applications. More specific to health care, frameworks are in place at Johns Hopkins and other large academic medical centers. Broad consents, such as the ones employed at Vanderbilt and the Mayo Clinic, could facilitate downstream uses of clinical data for development of robust machine learning models. Aside from the consent process, any research study involving patient data needs to be approved by institutional review boards (IRBs), which consist of senior researchers and act as impartial evaluators of the risks involved with the study. And if data are involved, data trust committees specifically evaluate the risks to misuses of data, and data-use agreements govern the ethical use and distribution of clinically relevant data. Community members may also become involved in the process of determining ethical research.

Blending a guideline such as the one from Google and clinical elements suggests an ethical framework for health care AI software development that could benefit from these features:

1. Issue clear consent for use of the clinical data, ideally broad consent, which allows use of the data for multiple machine learning models that may have different outputs. (In many places, broad consents for these purposes are already in use.)
2. Evaluation of model bias by technical stakeholder and explained in terms that a user understands; this evaluation could be facilitated by an impartial technical stakeholder (in academia, data trust committees serve as impartial stakeholders).

3. Evaluation of clinical benefit by clinical stakeholder in a way that an end user understands.
4. A mechanism to inform data owner(s) of the significance/results of the use of their data. (Note: Here, data owner could mean a study participant. Since machine learning models rely on data from many participants, contacting each participant individually might not be feasible, but some mass communication could work and would still give the participant insight into how their data were used.)

Since software continues to change, frameworks defining the ethical development of health care AI tools will also need to change with time. Each organization may have slightly different needs, but the guidelines above could serve as a starting point for discussion for internal stakeholders.

PART 3:
OPPORTUNITIES

CHAPTER 7:

MENTORSHIP, ROBOTICS, AND NEURONS

How on earth do what we understand to be tangles of neurons, cells—sparking, popping, and communicating with each other—lead to this fluid experience?

—ERIC HORVITZ, TECHNICAL FELLOW AND
DIRECTOR OF MICROSOFT RESEARCH LABS[127]

During my junior year of college, I took a course on neurobiology and was fascinated by how neural synapses work. During the summer between my junior and senior years, I completed a neurophysiology internship under the guidance of Michelle Mynlieff at Marquette University. The field of neuroscience brings together concepts in mathematics, biology, and cognition, and at the time, I had little awareness of the field of AI, let alone neural networks. And, to be fair, the field of AI hadn't yet become "mainstream." Little did I know at the time that the concepts I was learning in my undergraduate neuroscience class had already been

---

127 Eric Horvitz, "AI and Our Future with Machines with Dr. Eric Horvitz." December 4, 2017, in *Microsoft Research Podcast*, podcast, 26:12.

implemented by computer scientists and medical researchers to lay a significant foundation for predictive tools, and the momentum to build health care AI tools had begun to grow.

Some of the computational tools used in AI are inspired by the operation of living neurons. Tools like neural networks crudely imitate the communication between neurons, which interlink with each other and enable decision-making, motor functions, and emotional responses. Neural networks in AI resemble neuronal function only superficially since the two systems have mutually exclusive features at their cores. Neural networks are being explored in biology but are not fully copied in computer science; neurobiology remains fertile ground for new ideas in the field, and perhaps data scientists will continue to learn from biologists.

ERIC HORVITZ AND FINDING INSPIRATION

Eric Horvitz knew from a young age—around fourth or fifth grade—that he would be doing science. Horvitz is now a technical fellow at Microsoft and directs Microsoft Research Lab. His credentials from Stanford are impressive, but his fascination with and excitement for improving health care with technology are the intangible factors that drive his career and spark new ideas. As a graduate student studying computer science and medicine in the 1990s, Horvitz recalls that he couldn't get there all at once. Horvitz was inspired by and interested in a variety of research areas, so he took a stepwise approach of getting closer to finding his passion by talking with research laboratories he found interesting and identifying academic mentors.[128]

Identifying academic mentors is a very important concept and a key to self-growth and development. In medicine and other fields, self-directed and lifelong learning is a requirement for continued growth and for staying intrigued with the field.

Horvitz realized he loved what he was doing and decided to embrace it. Early on in graduate school, Horvitz was very interested in applying predictive models to time-critical areas like trauma care and aerospace, and given his interest in human cognition, he began creating models of human decision-making.[129]

One of Horvitz's projects focuses on the observation that among hospitalized patients discharged from the hospital, 20 percent are readmitted to the hospital within thirty days. This problem represents a significant clinical and societal cost. So, Horvitz and his team looked at ten years of hospital data, which included twenty-two thousand variables, and built a system that predicts when the discharged patient might come back to the hospital. A dataset of that size would be impossible to analyze by hand or with human eyes alone. Enter machine learning algorithms that can crunch and make sense of those clinical variables. This system is used in hospitals worldwide and allows the treating physicians

---

128 Ibid.

129 "Making Friends with Artificial Intelligence: Eric Horvitz at TEDx-Austin," TEDxAustin, accessed on September 29, 2019.

to tailor follow-up plans to patients in an attempt to reduce readmissions to the hospital.

Physicians see many patients and are trained to understand patterns, but surprises happen. Not every diagnosis is perfect, and patients return to the hospital for unexpected reasons. So Horvitz and his team created a model that trains on previous clinical surprises and alerts the physician if it detects a high likelihood of a clinical surprise. As described by Horvitz, the surprise alert could appear along these lines to the physician: This patient you are discharging will likely come back with a primary diagnosis nowhere in the chart. Do you want to take a look?[130] This alert empowers the physician to look deeper into the patient history and then contact the patient to intervene before the next adverse event.

The medical interventions pursued by Horvitz are wide-reaching, given their implementation in large hospital systems. Implementing these new systems is costly, however, and administrative hurdles exist. These realities apply to any moonshot ideas and require significant support, such as from hospital leadership and from their commercial partners who are increasingly focused on growth and exploration.

At Microsoft, CEO Satya Nadella seeks to cultivate an ethos of growth and exploration by changing Microsoft's culture from a fixed, know-it-all culture to a growth mindset that's open to learning and trying new approaches.[131] These new

---

130 Ibid.

131 Satya Nadella, "Can Microsoft's chief Satya Nadella restore it to glory?" *Financial Times*, October 13, 2017.

approaches are required for the success of any health care AI moonshot idea, including Horvitz's projects, and are congruent with self-directed and lifelong learning.

Microsoft is not alone in its openness to trying new approaches, learning from mistakes, and focusing on growth. And these qualities are scalable to any health care AI moonshot idea, including the pursuits of recreating the human brain, robotic surgery, and using open-source software to make robotic technology available to new groups.

OPENAI AND THE HUMAN BRAIN

The efforts of OpenAI make one wonder: how far can we go in the field of AI? OpenAI develops artificial general intelligence with the mission of ensuring that AI helps all of humanity.[132] As its name suggests, the company makes contributions to the open-source community and uses open-source programming tools, such as Python. As of this writing, OpenAI has ninety-one repos in GitHub.[133]

Within the tech community, the development groups writing AI code connect closely to the sources of capital that support nascent technology (i.e., venture capital funds, large companies, angel investors). As an example, Microsoft has a significant financial commitment to OpenAI. Early in 2019, Microsoft invested a whopping billion dollars into OpenAI's

132 "Discovering and enacting the path to safe artificial general intelligence," OpenAI, accessed on March 31, 2020,

133 "OpenAI," GitHub, accessed on March 31, 2020.

initiative to replicate the human brain.[134] OpenAI's brain initiative has applications that reach beyond health care, as the vision for the brain initiative is to create a general cognitive decision-making tool that can run all of Microsoft's software systems.

OpenAI cofounder and CTO Greg Brockman and his team are focused on replicating capabilities of the human brain from a computational perspective. From a biology angle, researchers at MIT are also visualizing live neurons as they compute. Edward Boyden, who leads the synthetic neurobiology group at the MIT Media Lab, uses a technique that illuminates brain cells when they are electrically active and then links the activity of cells to specific behaviors.[135] For some context, the human brain has about one hundred billion neurons, and the technique used by Boyden allows scientists to observe activity for about ten neurons at a time. The group hopes to scale the technique and apply it to predict neural computations. Since neural networks are modeled after the functioning of neurons, further understanding may inform the development of new machine learning methods.

Boyden is not the first—or only—neuroscientist researcher who has used methods to calculate and observe when neurons are firing. What makes Boyden's technique special is its noninvasive approach to observing how neurons behave compared to more invasive techniques such as in-vivo patch

---

134 Richard Waters, "Microsoft invests \$1bn in OpenAI effort to replicate human brain," *Financial Times*, July 22, 2019.

135 Anne Trafton, "New method visualizes groups of neurons as they compute," MIT Media Lab via MIT News, October 9, 2019.

clamp. Visualizing actual neural networks will give computer scientists more ideas about how the brain works and how to construct new neural network software that continues to build on today's open-source tools.

ROBOTS IN HEALTH CARE—NOT ALWAYS AI

Robotics play a significant role in health care, and research into integration of AI and robotics is underway. A common public perception of AI conjures images of a robot, and while some AI-assisted robotics are used in health care, I should clarify that not all robotics in health care are representations of AI.

NON-AI ROBOTICS

Robotic surgery works effectively without artificial intelligence. But robot-assisted and even robot-controlled surgeries have certain advantages. In 2000, the FDA approved robotic surgery with the da Vinci Surgical System, which has been rapidly adopted by hospitals worldwide for use in the treatment of a wide range of conditions, including heart surgery and minimally invasive abdominal and urologic surgeries.[136,137] Today, over five thousand da Vinci systems are used at hospitals worldwide.[138] While no current da Vinci systems

---

136 "Overview: Robotic Surgery," Mayo Foundation for Medical Education and Research, accessed on January 10, 2020.

137 "Robotic Prostatectomy," Johns Hopkins Medicine, accessed on January 22, 2020.

138 "Pairing human ingenuity with technology," Intuitive, accessed on October 29, 2019.

use AI, its main benefits include minimal invasiveness and the ability to use small, high-definition cameras to show the condition of internal tissue. Robotic technology alone does not constitute the use of AI; rather, AI can improve the way robotic surgeries work by learning from previous experiences.

COMPUTER-INTEGRATED SURGERY

Within the computer science department at Johns Hopkins University, researchers train robots to observe while a surgeon applies stitches to learn the various nuances of these movements. The apparently straightforward motions of forming stitches reveal many important details: how to create an effective stitch over a particular contour of the skin, how to tie the stitch, how to undo the stitch when necessary, how long it takes to perform the stitch. Greg Hager leads the Language of Surgery effort, which is an interdisciplinary collaboration between computer engineers, surgeons, and statisticians.[139] Robots begin to understand human surgeons by watching every stitch and then learning the most effective techniques, with the goal of augmenting the movements of human surgeons.

Microsoft's Horvitz describes this process with admiration, as he imagines a world where robots are not adversarial or competitive, but rather understand humans so deeply that they complement us.[140] Developing the technology is

---

139 "Dissecting the Language of Surgery," Johns Hopkins University, accessed on January 25, 2020.

140 Eric Horvitz, "AI and Our Future with Machines with Dr. Eric Horvitz." December 4, 2017, in *Microsoft Research Podcast*, podcast, 26:12.

expensive and time-consuming, and the confines of academic medical centers like Johns Hopkins are a perfect place to incubate this technology. With the right support, such as the process outlined by Cochran at the JHHCS, technologies like robot-assisted stitching could be expanded to additional medical centers and to underserved populations. Robot-assisted stitching is still a research effort. As a simple gut check: what would it take for you to trust an autonomous robot to stitch your arm after surgery?

On the surface level (no pun intended), automation of the stitching process may seem trivial. Yet stitching is a somewhat overlooked area that could benefit from process improvement. An estimated forty-four million soft-tissue surgeries are performed in the United States each year that require stitching. Complications can be costly, sometimes painful, and can result in secondary infections or other adverse outcomes. In colorectal surgery alone, improper connection of intestine segments with stitches can lead to a leak and subsequently intra-abdominal infection, which occurs nearly 20 to 30 percent of cases.[141]

RAVEN AND STAR

Complications related to suturing, whether for surgeries or wounds, has led to the development of automated suturing using AI. The first version of the Raven Surgical Robot was developed at the University of Washington, and a second

---

141 Arthur Hirsch, "Johns Hopkins scientist programs robot to perform 'soft tissue' surgery," Johns Hopkins University, accessed on January 4, 2020.

version (Raven II) was developed by the University of Washington and the University of California–Santa Cruz. This second version can be found at Berkeley and about twenty other institutions, where its development continues. In 2013, a team of researchers at Berkeley reported an overall success rate of 87 percent to perform suturing for laparoscopic surgery.[142]

A similar tool, the Smart Tissue Autonomous Robot (STAR) system, is intended to be used under surgeon supervision; it uses a 3D imaging system and a near-infrared sensor to identify fluorescent markers along the edges of the tissue to keep the needle on track.[143] STAR was initially developed at the Children's National Medical Center (CNMC) in Washington, DC. Axel Krieger (now faculty at the University of Maryland) and Simon Leonard (now faculty at Johns Hopkins) contributed to the development of STAR at CNMC. These technologies began with well-defined and somewhat narrow use cases, but their performance is promising.

If development continues, these systems could assist human surgeons by freeing up their time to address less routine surgical tasks or by helping a surgeon who has been in the operating room for hours and needs a break. We should note that these technologies are still in development, so for both Raven and STAR, a time frame for when these robotic

142 John Schulman, et al, "A Case Study of Trajectory Transfer Through Non-Rigid Registration for a Simplified Suturing Scenario," Berkeley University.

143 Arthur Hirsch, "Johns Hopkins scientist programs robot to perform 'soft tissue' surgery," Johns Hopkins University, accessed on January 4, 2020.

systems will be implemented in clinical settings is unclear. In other areas of health care AI, the moonshot is becoming closer to reality.

DEVELOPMENT OF OPEN-SOURCE TOOLS TO MAKE DA VINCI MORE ACCESSIBLE FOR RESEARCH

Advances in surgical devices are developing quickly. The tools are becoming smaller and more responsive. These surgical devices can capture high-definition images for use downstream in other AI-enabled tools, such as for pathology diagnosis, and by algorithms that predict disease progression using image data. Given the progression of surgical devices and the continual advancement of complementary AI software, the da Vinci system first introduced in 2000 represents only the first step of what is possible for robot-assisted surgery. Since its introduction, da Vinci has developed four generations of systems. Johns Hopkins acquired a da Vinci system in 2009 although the mechanical parts for the da Vinci were acquired earlier, in 2004, for research and led to the development of the da Vinci Research Kit (dVRK), according to Peter Kazanzides—a codeveloper of dVRK.[144]

Kazanzides and computer science professor Russell Taylor developed an "open-source mechatronics" system called dVRK, consisting of the electronics, firmware, and software needed to control first-generation da Vinci systems.[145] The

---

144 "The dVRK Allows Worldwide Research in Robotic Surgery," Laboratory for Computational Sensing and Robotics, Johns Hopkins University, accessed on January 15, 2020.

145 Ibid.

dVRK does not have FDA approval and therefore cannot be used on humans; it is intended to provide an affordable system for researchers. Their software is available on Github, and more than thirty-five institutions worldwide are using dVRK.[146]

Open-source software enables groups to use equipment that is a decade old to perform research intended to improve surgeries and related outcomes. The dVRK open-source software provides a less expensive option for researchers, and it finds a use for the da Vinci systems being retired from the operating room (i.e., by recycling them for researchers). According to Kazanzides, researchers obtain the hardware from the hospital, by donation from the company, and some researchers have even purchased a da Vinci on eBay, with prices ranging from about $10,000 to $40,000—a significant discount compared to about $1 million for the original cost of a da Vinci. While the manufacturer of da Vinci provides an API that allows the researcher to collect measurements from the robot, the dVRK allows the researcher to control the robot.

Combining the fields of computer science, neurobiology, and human cognition is becoming more reality than science fiction. And while the field of robotics is decades old, the open-source community is finding ways to make surgical robots more accessible to the medical research community. In the following chapters, we'll observe the growing trend of open-source software in AI and explore the interplay between academia, industry, and financial backers.

---

146 "Da Vinci Research Kit," GitHub, accessed on January 3, 2020.

CHAPTER 8:

A LEG UP: PATHOLOGY AND PROSTHESES

We call it digital pathology now, but this is shifting to the standard of care. Eventually, this will just be called pathology, and our company will be leading the way.

—DAVID WEST, FOUNDER OF PROSCIA[147]

When I think about moving my legs, neural signals from my central nervous system pass through my nerves and activate muscles within my limbs. Electrodes sense these signals, and small computers in the bionic limb decode the nerve pulses into my intended movement patterns. Stated simply—when I think about moving, that command is communicated to the synthetic part of my body.

—HUGH HERR, DOUBLE AMPUTEE AND HEAD OF BIOMECHATRONICS AT MIT MEDIA LAB[148]

---

147 "Pathology's Digital Future," Johns Hopkins Biomedical Engineering, accessed on November 14, 2019.

148 Hugh Herr, "How we'll become cyborgs and extend human potential," TED, accessed on July 19, 2019.

Hospital pathology departments are staffed with physicians and support staff who process, analyze, and store human biopsy tissue taken during surgical procedures. Depending on the tissue and the diagnostic need, microscope slides are prepared using the tissue and various stains that allow a microscope to inspect certain cell types. The process of creating and storing slides is fairly laborious since the tissue needs to be sectioned, placed on a microscope slide, stained, catalogued, and analyzed.

As a part-time graduate student at Johns Hopkins, I joined the Hopkins Biotech Network (HBN) and became a member of the executive board. I wanted to meet other students and staff interested in entrepreneurship and also to learn about different research areas within the Hopkins ecosystem. Fellow HBN members were pursuing advanced degrees in basic science, public health, business, and design. Our dynamic group invited professors and students to discuss their pioneering work in order to inspire students interested in the field of biotechnology and to cultivate mentor-mentee relationships. The topics of HBN events ranged from stem cells to biotechnology commercialization to applications of AI in pathology. At an HBN event, I first learned about digital pathology and David West's then nascent company, Proscia. (David claims that someday digital pathology will simply become *pathology*, but the distinction exists today to highlight the AI-assisted form of pathology.)

From humble beginnings, Proscia has grown significantly since its founding in 2014. Many digital health tools are developed by private companies like Proscia that depend on external funding to test and scale their initial ideas. External funds come from venture capital firms, angel investors, competitive incubators like Y Combinator, or some combination. Investment in digital health tools focused on AI has exploded in recent years. According to Rock Health, $1.4 billion was invested across sixty-six deals in digital health companies using AI in 2019, bringing total funding to $6.8 billion across 383 deals since 2011. Proscia's humble beginnings and initial hurdles are par for the course for early-stage health AI companies, and since its founding, it has gained very stable VC funding and support from an impressive technical team.

Proscia is focused on developing AI technology that reads images of millions of pathology slides and learns patterns from those slides, ultimately to facilitate a diagnosis based on tissue morphology. To someone outside the field of health AI, this endeavor may seem niche, but other companies who develop technology are supporting digital pathology. PathAI, led by Stanford and MIT graduates, collaborates with pathologists in clinical labs, drug companies, and global health nonprofits with the goal of assisting pathologists in making rapid and reliable diagnoses for the patient, similar to Proscia.[149] Like Proscia, PathAI is supported by venture capital funding, and in April 2019, PathAI secured $60 million in Series B funding to further expand the company.[150] Another group, Paige.AI, focuses specifically on improving cancer

---

149 "Pathology Evolved: Advanced learning toward faster, more accurate diagnosis of disease," PathAI, accessed on February 1, 2020.

150 Tiffany Freitas, "PathAI Secures $60M in Series B Funding Led by General Atlantic and Existing Investor General Catalyst," Businesswire, April 17, 2019.

diagnosis by using AI to assist pathologists.[151] Paige.AI is a newcomer to the digital pathology industry. It was launched in February 2018 with $25 million in Series A venture capital funding and with the support of renowned cancer center Memorial Sloan Kettering in New York City.[152,153]

Yet another digital pathology group, Deep Lens, combines AI and pathology to identify and triage patients for clinical trials much sooner than traditional methods, resulting in better outcomes and stronger recruitment in clinical trials.[154] Deep Lens was developed at Nationwide Children's Hospital in Cincinnati, Ohio, and has raised $3.2 million in seed funding.[155] Currently, a cancer diagnosis can be dismal for a variety of cancers, but we have also seen tremendous growth in the survival of patients with a previously terminal disease such as metastatic lung cancer or melanoma, due to the advancement of therapies (immunotherapy) via clinical trials. In the setting of cancer, when drug therapies can be limited or fraught with side effects, Deep Lens evaluates for

---

151 "Paige: We are transforming the diagnosis and treatment of cancer," PAIGE, accessed on March 31, 2020.

152 Conor Hale, "MSKCC-backed digital pathology startup nets FDA breakthrough device designation," FierceBiotech, March 7, 2019.

153 Ingrid Lunden, "PaigeAI nabs $25M, inks IP deal with Sloan Kettering to bring machine learning to cancer pathology," TechCrunch, February 5, 2018.

154 "Matching the right patient with the right trial at the right time" Deep Lens, accessed on July 10, 2019.

155 Jonah Comstock, "Digital pathology startup Deep Lens raises $3.2M," MobiHealth News, accessed on August 12, 2019.

clinical trials available at the time of the cancer diagnosis and based on the specimen of tumor that is biopsied.

Two common threads in each of these digital pathology companies are their origins in academia and their ability to garner support from venture capital firms for initial investment to scale and further test their ideas. The story of David West, cofounder of Proscia, exemplifies the long and uncertain journey of many of these companies. West's entry into the world of entrepreneurship began in the Philadelphia suburbs, although not initially in biotechnology. As early as seventh grade, West and his friends started a business converting VHS videos to DVDs.[156] These early lessons in entrepreneurship proved useful in later years when West founded multiple biotech-related companies, notably Proscia. David graduated with a bachelor of science in bioengineering and biomedical engineering from Johns Hopkins University in 2016, at which time he cofounded Karcinex (2012), and then Proscia.

THE DATA

From a technology perspective, West sees a bigger opportunity gap in digital pathology than in any other field of medicine. That opportunity gap begins with data. Historically, microscope slides were stored in physical cabinets at only one location, inaccessible to machine learning tools. Each slide is a piece of glass that holds a tiny slice of preserved tissue. Within each slide is a story, a snapshot of a biological narrative trapped in time. That biological story manifests itself

---

156 "Pathology's Digital Future," Johns Hopkins Biomedical Engineering, web page, January 11, 2019.

on a cellular level and is interpreted by a pathologist, who examines the cells microscopically and determines whether the tissue is in a healthy state, whether disease has progressed, and if so how far. West's digital pathology tools digitize that story to store and transmit its data, largely free of the constraints of a physical glass slide. Slides that were once stored in physical file cabinets in hospital corridors can now be represented in a digital, machine-readable format in the cloud. The slides and their information are now being reinterpreted by AI tools for interpretation and electronic storage.

At Johns Hopkins, about a million pathology slides are created every year. With the tools that West and his team have developed, these slides can be converted to digital images. The converted slide images are large even by today's standards. Most of the pathology images processed by Proscia are around one gigabyte scanned at full resolution. Some fluorescent images exceed thirty gigabytes each. These file sizes imply significant storage requirements, since each patient may have a record containing three hundred to four hundred individual slides from multiple tissue biopsy sites. When stored as digital images on computer servers, these data represent tremendous opportunities for new discoveries. AI-driven pathology aims to systematically understand the biological story embedded in those slides after they have become accessible digitally. Since the AI tools require millions of cases to learn the patterns and subtle factors that indicate disease, diagnoses can be made more quickly and more accurately.

The idea of Proscia was inspired by West's many talks with Johns Hopkins urology researchers during his time as an undergraduate student. Specifically, he was inspired by distinguished Johns Hopkins professor and prostate cancer expert Donald Coffey and by the work of Johns Hopkins urology researcher Bob Veltri, who studies biomarkers for prostate and bladder cancers. Some consider Coffey's research a bedrock upon which modern genetic and epigenetic discoveries at Johns Hopkins were built, including his revelation that the cell nucleus has a skeleton, which he dubbed the nuclear matrix.[157] West was enamored by the technology they were using and developing. West also sees Eric Topol as a luminary of AI applications to health care problems and admires his ability to create digestible content for a diverse audience. By working alongside established and passionate scientists, David reflects that he found it "hard to avoid catching the bug" of working within medical research.

Eventually, what started out as a fun project eventually grew and became a market opportunity. West and his team operate in a world dominated by glass slides and their cumbersome storage, and West forecasts a transition to completely digital pathology image storage in the next five years. Currently, digital pathology represents an approximate $24 billion market with potentially $100 billion in market opportunity in the next five years, according to West.

While West was excited about the technology being developed for Proscia and about the potential to bring the technology to market, he admits he lacked expertise in navigating funding, especially as a recent college graduate. During the early

---

157 Amy Mone, "Johns Hopkins cancer pioneer Donald Coffey dies at 85," Johns Hopkins University, accessed on November 11, 2019.

days of Proscia, as an undergraduate student, West recalls hearing "no" answers from about 98 percent of the investors he approached. However, the even-keeled West understands that something can be learned from every encounter with investors, so he persisted. To an investor inundated with pitch decks advertising new technologies with bold claims on how AI will change the world, West had to prove his idea had merit. Investors are cautious, harkening back to Cochran's warning about "flavors of the month," and they closely evaluate the validity of underlying technology and its claims. West knew he had a good idea and valuable data. To get Proscia started, he only needed one initial investor to believe in his vision.

Proscia is currently a thirty-person company, including a product team, engineering, sales, and a back office. About a third of Proscia's employees have a PhD, and West humbly claims he's the least qualified in the company. West is proud to say he's backed by supportive strategic and financial advisers. One of his first investors, Neil Cohen of Emerald Development Managers, now serves on Proscia's board of directors. As of today, multiple investors support Proscia, including Flybridge Capital, Robinhood Ventures, and Fusion Fund—all of whom invest in early-stage companies.

PROSTHESES

AI may still seem like an abstract concept. After all, for these tools to work, intangible data are analyzed by machines that retrieve data from an ethereal cloud. And yes, neural networks are running behind the scenes in the tools developed by West and others, but many other scientists and entrepreneurs are also incorporating these computational techniques to build tangible applications for AI. We saw some examples of those products as robotics tools in the previous chapter. One of the pioneers in the field of health AI and robotics is Hugh Herr, who has found ways to integrate AI with prosthetics.

Traditional prostheses are cumbersome and often feel unnatural; while they are functional, they do not always support the full range of motion of natural limbs. Additionally, these passive extensions do not enable a user to generate force from the artificial limb. Machines are capable of making quick, complex calculations, such as those required for human motor skills, but interfacing with them has been a challenge. AI can bridge the gap between a user's intended movement and the quick responsiveness and power of a mechanical system to provide for a machine-aided or active prosthesis. Distance, speed, force, and environment are all factors relevant to functional prostheses, and, according to Megan Molteni of *Wired*, researchers are training artificial limbs to make specific and nuances decisions, such as how quickly to accelerate toward a cup of coffee, and what kind of grip is needed to pick it up.[158] (It's not an easy problem to solve, but the rewards regarding quality of life are tremendous.)

Kirsten Dahlgren is one patient whose life has been completely changed by the use of AI-assisted prostheses. Formerly a competitive dancer, she needed a foot amputation due to

---

158 Megan Molteni, "Want a True Bionic Limb? Good Luck Without Machine Learning," *Wired*, May 3, 2017.

an injury sustained while traveling.[159] Her prosthetic leg is assisted by AI, which senses the muscles and can respond to her intended movement. With the help of her AI-assisted prosthesis, she now has aspirations to snowboard again and dance at her wedding. Development of this technology is led by Hugh Herr, head of the Biomechatronics group at MIT Media Lab, who is himself a double amputee.

Given the examples of West and Herr, we can clearly see that investment in AI to support clinical needs is not misguided, and the impacts on society and quality of life are significant. Perhaps one day soon, the AI technology being developed by Herr and others will be combined with open-source 3D-printed prostheses.[160,161] Prostheses are expensive, and while 3D-printed prostheses lack the refinement of commercially manufactured prostheses available in the United States, combining AI technologies developed by Herr and others with the affordability and portability of 3D-printing techniques could lead to devices that improve quality of life in far corners of the world.

West, founder of Proscia, acknowledges that one can easily get caught up in the early hubris of momentum as a startup builds and blossoms. Proscia and all the technologies

---

159 "How AI is helping patients with prosthetics," *Today*, September 30, 2019.

160 "E-nable Is Growing," Enabling the Future, accessed on August 12, 2019.

161 "3-D Printed Prosthetic Hand Fit for a Superhero," as seen in the 2016 Biennial Report, Johns Hopkins University, accessed on September 7, 2019.

mentioned in this chapter are in their early stages. The technologies are new, and perhaps risky, but the potential benefits are enormous for developers, investors, providers, and patients.

CHAPTER 9:

DRUG DISCOVERY
AND DEVELOPMENT

———

We deal with vast amounts of very fragmented and diverse data. No human could analyze or make useful insights of the current amount of data in their lifetime— it's like looking for a needle in a haystack. So we need computers to augment our ability to consume these data and make useful insights.

—MAGDALENA ZWIERZYNA, BIOMEDICAL
DATA SCIENTIST AT BENEVOLENTAI[162]

The drug manufacturers are in the business of discovering and creating new drugs. Drug manufacturers constantly ask themselves: How can we get new drugs to the market? Where can we find new expertise to support drug discovery and development? And, ultimately, how can we improve the quality of life? Increasingly, drug manufacturers are turning to new databases and to machine learning to generate more drug candidates and to accelerate drug discovery.

———

162 *NVIDIA.* "Nvidia and BenevolentAI—Accelerating Scientific Discovery with AI."

Nick Zachos, a researcher at the Johns Hopkins University School of Medicine, studies molecular mechanisms responsible for diarrhea. While diarrhea may seem quotidian to some of us, it's a significant public health issue and can be clinically severe. Its causes include chronic illnesses like Crohn's Disease as well as acute food-borne illnesses and cholera. Zachos and others have developed novel techniques to understand the molecular pathways responsible for diarrhea with the goal of developing therapeutics.

Academic researchers like Zachos generate data and publish their findings, which are peer-reviewed and used by fellow researchers to generate new ideas. Until recently, reviewing peer-reviewed literature was typically done by the individual, but companies like BenevolentAI are creating AI tools that systematically read the literature to uncover hidden knowledge and generate new ideas.

The general approach of drug development begins with the following questions: What are the current therapeutic needs? What do we know about those diseases? Have those diseases been modeled in laboratory experiments, and have those models been validated in humans? If we pursue drug development for this particular therapeutic need, could we generate profit? Published research findings are a rich source of clues to these questions and build on decades of work from thousands of authors. In systematic and objective ways, machine learning tools can mine publication data to understand molecular pathways that have been tested by research groups and the outcomes of research.

Machine learning tools can search for deviations in specific pathways that are being targeted for therapeutic development. Are there pathways and molecules that haven't yet been explored? If groups like BenevolentAI identify a novel pathway, they then need to prove why it's important, which is where groups like Zachos' fit into the picture. To machine learning developers, groups like Zachos' serve as good collaborators, given their experience testing drug candidates in animal or human models. Zachos' group has experience developing human enteroids, which are cellular structures derived from human cells.

While enteroids are created in controlled environments and do not interact with other human systems, their response to chemical compounds approximates actual human bodily response and can be measured. Using intestinal stem cells, Zachos' group develops enteroids to model IBD, which can be used to quickly test drug candidates identified by BenevolentAI. The process of early drug screening (i.e., testing the chemistry behind a potentially newly discovered disease pathway) is a necessary step before clinical trials. The collaboration facilitated by Zachos and BenevolentAI builds on years of developments in stem cell biology and machine learning and represents a new paradigm for accelerated drug discovery.

* * *

During my undergraduate education at Marquette University, I enjoyed organic chemistry—a sometimes unpopular and controversial opinion. I took the version of organic chemistry intended for chemistry majors, which was a more detailed course compared to the standard organic chemistry class intended for biochemistry majors. Organic chemistry is a term that sometimes sparks a twinge of anxiety even in science majors at US universities. Most people entrenched in university life, even nonscience majors, know this. Organic chemistry has a reputation of being hard. However, the subject has many practical and exciting applications, including the discovery of new drugs.

As a commuter student as a college sophomore, I sometimes arrived on campus before my morning classes started, to study and wake up in the library over a fresh cup of coffee. I felt a kind of satisfaction in writing out organic chemistry reactions and wondering if the compounds I was simulating on paper could ever be developed in commercial laboratories. In particular, radical reactions fascinated me. A radical, or free radical, is any chemical compound that contains a free electron. Under certain conditions, these chemicals react aggressively with nonradicals, often in chain reactions. In nutrition, "superfoods" are lauded for their high content of antioxidants—chemicals whose properties can stop the chain reaction caused by free radicals. In disease, free radicals play a significant role; reactive oxygen species (ROS) are one type of free radical that contributes to programmed cell death.

Many antioxidants work by stimulating enzymes, a type of protein, to perform chemical reactions on carcinogenic compounds that are circulating in the body. Public health researchers John Groopman, Thomas Kensler, and others study how antioxidants found in broccoli sprouts might mitigate the effect of carcinogens found in airborne pollution.[163,164,165] Free radicals have some less pernicious roles too. If you open a bottle of cooking oil that has stood for a long time, you will notice the hiss of air entering the bottle. Since the last time it was opened, oxygen in the bottle has been consumed by a free radical reaction (autoxidation) between the oxygen and the surface of the oil, which slightly reduced the volume of air and caused the negative pressure within the bottle.[166]

Aside from the chemical reactions themselves, I also wondered about the process of commercialization. If someone is successful in manufacturing the chemical compound, how are those compounds tested for efficacy, and how are they sold? For a college sophomore sitting in my organic chemistry lecture, the process of drug discovery sometimes seemed out of reach and theoretical. My organic chemistry instructor, Dr. Daniel Sem, illuminated many of the processes of drug discovery and drug development, based on his earlier experiences in the pharmaceutical industry.

---

163 Patricia Egner, et al, "Bioavailability of Sulforaphane from Two Broccoli Sprout Beverages: Results of a Short-term, Cross-over Clinical Trial in Qidong, China." *Cancer Prevention Research* 4, no. 3 (2011). 384.

164 Thomas Kensler, et al, "Modulation of the metabolism of airborne pollutants by glucoraphanin-rich and sulforaphane-rich broccoli sprout beverages in Qidong, China." *Carcinogenesis.* 33, no. 1 (2011): 101.

165 Patricia Egner, et al, "Rapid and sustainable detoxication of airborne pollutants by broccoli sprout beverage: results of a randomized clinical trial in China." *Cancer Prevention Research* 7, no. 8 (2014): 813.

166 William Brown, Christopher Foote, Brent Iverson, *Organic Chemistry* (Belmont, CA.: Thomson Brooks/Cole, 2005), 316.

Prior to entering academia, Sem cofounded a drug development company, Triad Therapeutics, in San Diego, which was bought by Novartis. In terms of volume, Novartis is one of the largest producers of medicines in the world, with over seventy billion doses per year across a wide range of therapeutic areas.[167] Sem is now a professor of pharmaceutical studies and the dean of the Batterman School of Business at Concordia University, where he also directs technology transfer for the university. Before joining Concordia as a dean, Sem also helped people start companies although he found it a struggle to connect scientists with businesspeople.

Sem admits that his first passion is science, but he realized he wanted to be more involved with commercializing medical research. When the opportunity arose to become dean of a business school, he thought he could bridge the gap between scientific development and commercialization. Given his experience, which straddles commercial biotechnology and academic research, Sem believes an interplay between both fields is needed to bring discoveries to the bedside.

Academia excels at teaching the difficult, abstract topics in organic chemistry and exploring initial candidates in drug discovery. However, academia has generally lacked the capacity to test, promote, and commercialize these compounds. In order to bring candidate drugs from the academic bench to your neighborhood pharmacy, academia needs to connect with industry to bring ideas and candidate drugs to scale. The partnership between Zachos and BenevolentAI is a good

---

167 Vas Narasimhan, et al, "Science, Business, and Innovation in Big Pharma: A Conversation with Novartis' CEO," Andreessen Horowitz.

example of new academia-industry partnerships that stand to accelerate drug discovery and development.

DRUG DISCOVERY, DRUG DEVELOPMENT, AND CLINICAL TRIALS

Drug discovery and drug development are different but related processes. Drug discovery is the process of identifying a chemical compound that interacts with a cellular target relevant to addressing a clinical problem. Much time and effort are devoted to the drug discovery process. Sometimes candidate drugs are discovered by bioprospecting—discovering bioreactive compounds from plants. Sometimes candidate drugs are discovered by finding alternative uses to existing prescription medications (i.e., repurposing). And sometimes candidate drugs are discovered de novo, by creating brand new compounds that react to cellular binding sites. At least for the approaches of finding alternative uses to existing prescription medications and creating completely new drug candidates, AI tools can expedite the process of drug discovery.

Groups including Alex Zhavoronkov of Insilico Medicine and others are using neural networks to produce candidate molecules. Neural networks are able to generate new molecules that researchers may have missed or hadn't thought of. In drug discovery, researchers use machine learning to identify new drug targets, screen known compounds for new therapeutic applications, and design new drug candidates.[168]

---

168 "Artificial Intelligence in Health Care: Benefits and Challenges of Machine Learning in Drug Development," Government Accountability Office, December 2019.

Implementing neural networks creates a more detailed mapping of how drug candidates could interact with a target cellular receptor.

Meanwhile, drug development is the process of testing and manufacturing the chemical compound. Some drug development occurs in academic research labs, although the process is primarily managed by large pharmaceutical companies. Drug discovery alone can take ten to twenty years, and the total cost ranges between $500 million and $2.6 billion.[169,170,171] The timeline for drug development includes vetting of the candidate drugs through clinical trials—a complex process governed by FDA regulations and limited by the availability of patients who agree to be part of the testing process. Clinical trials evaluate whether a candidate therapy shows efficacy in known healthy and clinically affected populations. Many clinical trials evaluate a newly discovered medication as part of this development phase. Figure 9.1 shows how use of machine learning augments the current process of drug development by enabling researchers to screen a greater number of compounds in a shorter amount of time.

---

169 Steven Paul, et al, "How to improve R&D productivity: the pharmaceutical industry's grand challenge." Nature Reviews Drug Discovery 9 (2010): 203.

170 Jerry Avorn. "The $2.6 Billion Pill—Methodologic and Policy Considerations." New England Journal of Medicine 372, 20 (2015): 1877.

171 Andrew Ward, "Big pharma seeks digital solution to productivity problem," Financial Times, April 1, 2016.

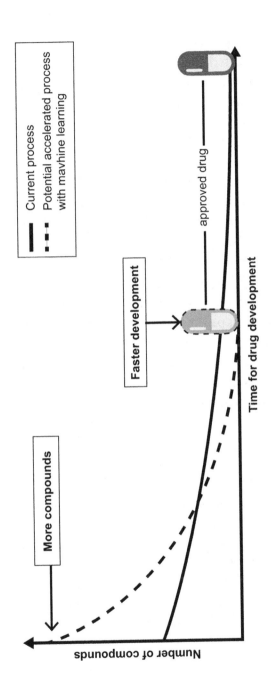

Figure 9.1: Augmenting the drug development process with machine learning.[172]

172 "Artificial Intelligence in Health Care: Benefits and Challenges of Machine Learning in Drug Development," Government Accountability Office, December 2019.

Deep Lens, mentioned in the previous chapter, develops AI to improve the clinical trials process, specifically the process of matching participants to clinical trials. This process entails identifying and filtering patients who are eligible for the study. The patients are screened with inclusion and exclusion criteria, which are lists of factors that define whether someone either can be included or is disqualified from participating in a research study, respectively. Age, demographic features, and medical conditions frequently appear in lists of inclusion and exclusion criteria. For example, a study to test the safety and efficacy of a blood pressure medication may seek patients between eighteen and seventy-five years of age (inclusion) who are not smokers (exclusion) and who are not currently taking any other blood pressure medication (exclusion). This process is lengthy. It requires patients to be identified for clinical trials of interest, and then a member of the research team to contact the patient to see if they formally qualify for the study. After an initial screening, the patient is evaluated in person, sometimes multiple times. This process is ripe for improvement since it can be inefficient and add time to drug development.

For drug manufacturers, the most forefront concern is candidate drug failure. Much attention is spent on selecting endpoint conditions for development termination. Stopping a drug in development would save considerable dollars and resources if those involved are informed the drug will likely fail, especially since the trial process takes years. On the other hand, premature termination of drug development results in huge potential revenue losses and missed opportunity for novel treatment of disease. Any drug that makes it through the development and selection process is a miracle and often involves staunch championship.

What if AI could determine the candidate therapy and if and when to terminate the development process? What if a computer program could automatically match patients to known clinical trials for the therapy based on their diagnosis and medical history? What if the computer program could both decrease the amount of back and forth between patients and the research team and create recommendations for specific clinical trials that are recruiting patients, therefore making the process more efficient and less costly? Deep Lens is developing predictive tools to best match patients and clinical trials, in an effort to expedite the recruitment of patients into clinical trials.

* * *

Sem comments that academia is "really good at the drug discovery and the biology behind it," and good at testing candidate drugs through development of in vitro models for showing efficacy of candidate drugs since candidate drugs are often tested on animal models before advancing to clinical trials. According to Sem, academia can afford to do higher-risk exploratory research, such as testing and proposing new drug candidates that may or may not be promoted to commercial production. In the context of drug discovery and development, the primary roles of academia favor drug discovery activities—such as proposing drug candidates—rather than drug development.

Generally speaking, in academia, Sem would always scan the literature for candidates. Industry can leverage the intellectual capital of academia to screen for higher-efficacy drugs. Industry-academia partnerships are necessary for completion of clinical trials prior to manufacturing of drug compounds by industry partners. Ultimately, to translate discoveries and knowledge from academia into drugs that are tested through clinical trials, manufactured, and available in a pharmacy, academics need a partnership with industry or someone from industry.

Both industry and academia benefit from the use of machine learning and AI. According to Sem, the process of drug development is relatively cookbook, and parts of discovery are routinized. However, he also cautions that some parts of discovery could never be replaced by AI, as a strong element of innovation prevails in the territory. Sem believes the industry will need a two-pronged approach to discovery that includes AI and non-AI approaches. For the parts of discovery that are systematic, use of AI tools can be scaled. As we've seen, AI tools are developed to understand patterns from historical data and to use those patterns to make predictions, given some new set of parameters. If computer models can learn to identify successful and unsuccessful drugs (specifically their chemical structures and complementary binding sites) and are given some new set of criteria (e.g., a new cellular receptor or protein structure), computer models can generate potential candidate drugs or some potential new targets to identify, saving time and money.

Adding to the already high financial cost of drug development, an estimated 30 to 50 percent of top-selling drugs do not work effectively in the patients who take them.[173] This gap represents a huge societal cost. While prescription drug

---

173 BenevolentAI, "How we work," accessed on October 15, 2019.

adherence is one reason for medication therapy failure, patient genetics are another, as genetic mutations can prevent patients from metabolizing a prescribed medication.[174] The fields of pharmacogenetics and pharmacogenomics study genetic markers to help understand variables including 1) prediction of adverse events, 2) prediction of efficacy, and 3) understanding the underlying disease or disorder. Whole genome sequencing has become routine and is facilitating precision medicine. One individual's genome could represent 500 GB of data, which can condense down to 20 GB or so when only looking for population differences. Analyzing two hundred people at once at 20 GB of data each quickly gets into the realm of big data and thus is now a research area developing very quickly.

Also, an estimated three hundred million people worldwide live and suffer with rare diseases whose treatment will not be developed under the current economic and drug development models.[175] These costs represent opportunities for tools like AI to bypass bottleneck steps in the development process and discover potential treatments in situations that are now considered niche. BenevolentAI is one group focused on using AI to fundamentally change the way drugs are developed and ambitiously aim to disrupt and remake the way medicines are developed so that no disease goes untreated.[176] Starting with the goal of creating the

---

174 Christina Warner, "The Future of Healthcare with Brad Bostic, CEO of hci," Thrive Global, December 12, 2019, accessed on December 18, 2019.

175 BenevolentAI, "How we work," accessed on October 15, 2019.

176 Ibid.

world's largest biomedical knowledge base, BenevolentAI has amassed over a billion machine-curated relationships, developed to guide the process of validating hypotheses and experiments.[177]

A paper published by members of the technical team of BenevolentAI describes some of the novel methods of generating new machine-curated relationships used in drug development. Using unsupervised and supervised methods, the team searches published literature to extract facts and relationships between genes and disease. The system developed by the team discovers relationships within published literature and then ranks and interprets the most salient patterns in a format that medical experts can interpret.[178]

The tools developed by BenevolentAI have little value in a silo, which is why BenevolentAI has made its tools interoperable for academic researchers and industry. The development of AI software has a strong open-source backbone, and some of the software tools developed by BenevolentAI can be modified and executed by anyone with the knowhow to develop computer programs. Think back to the example of TensorFlow: an open-source Python library developed by Google for deep learning.

---

177 Ibid.

178 Julien Fauqueur, Ashok Thillaisundaram, and Theodosia Togia, "Constructing large scale biomedical knowledge bases from scratch with rapid annotation of interpretable patterns," Cornell University, last revised on July 3, 2019.

Several years ago, open-source tools like TensorFlow were relatively niche. Now, online courses and academic courses are readily available to anyone who wants to know more about machine learning and deep learning. Even at the Johns Hopkins Bloomberg School of Public Health, machine learning was not offered as a course when I completed my MPH in 2014; now, a course on statistical machine learning using the open-source programming language R is available as an elective. As with all open-source computer programming tools, each version of the software includes improvements and enhancements. The same will hold true for the open-source tools developed by BenevolentAI. Soon, pharmaceutical development tools like the ones from BenevolentAI will be included in graduate school curricula and will be the subject of hackathons. These tools will create a paradigm shift in the availability and specificity of prescription drugs in the coming decades.

These ideas may seem farfetched and abstract, yet other industries have created open-source tools whose development has benefitted from crowdsourced groups, such as students and the general public. As a child, my brother and I puzzled over an early version of SETI@home—the free, crowdsourced software program supported by UC–Berkeley that analyzes radio telescope data, whose goal is to potentially find extraterrestrial intelligence.[179] The idea began in 1995 and was officially launched in 1999. To some, the idea of using an open-source tool to find extraterrestrial intelligence may seem far-fetched, but the notion of providing open-source tools to facilitate drug discovery is already in progress and has gained momentum.

179 SETI@home, "The science of SETI@home," University of California at Berkeley, accessed on February 20, 2020.

In 2000, a similar project geared toward computational drug design began at Stanford, led by the lab of Vijay Pande, who is also a general partner at Andreessen Horowitz, where he focuses on investments at the intersection of computer science and biomedical discovery. The Folding@home project is a distributed computing platform that simulates protein folding, which is one component of computational drug design. Folding@home is available for download on many computer platforms and is being put to use to potentially identify therapeutic antibody targets for COVID-19.[180] Crowdsourced computer programming could accelerate drug discovery by leveraging spare computational power from the general public and experts in academia and industry alike. Distributed tools like Folding@home enable you to run a computer program in the background of your home computer that could identify potential drug candidate treatments to rare diseases and pandemics.

CREDIBILITY OF PHARMA

A tension exists between the public and the pharmaceutical industry, especially in the United States. Prescription drugs can be prohibitively expensive yet can lead to large profits for pharmaceutical companies. Understandably, the public feels slighted. One useful definition of credibility comes from former Navy SEAL Chris Fussell, who defines credibility as the sum of proven competence, relationships, and integrity.[181]

180 Greg Bowman, "Folding@Home Takes Up the Fight Against COVID-19/ 2019-NCOV," Folding@Home, accessed on February 27, 2020.
181 Chris Fussell, *One Mission: How Leaders Build a Team of Teams* (New York, Portfolio/Penguin, 2017).

If this formula can extend to evaluating companies, where does credibility in big pharma stand?

While expertise and competence are clear, relationship with the public is not always a strength, as the public questions the integrity of big pharma when its profits are lopsided, considering the inaccessibility of prescription drugs for many Americans. Specialty drugs can cost patients and payers as much as $300,000 per year.[182] And some more mainstream drugs, like insulin, are relatively inexpensive to manufacture but expensive to purchase. Meanwhile, median household income in the United States is slightly north of $60,000. In other words, big pharma is currently failing the credibility test due to its perceived lack of integrity or sometimes less-than-favorable relationship with the public.

While big pharma is often vilified as money-gouging and unethical, its credibility should also take into account the positive contributions the pharmaceutical industry has made to disease management, not to mention the fact that the majority of scientists and physicians working in the pharmaceutical industry truly want to find cures and improve disease outcomes. Given the arguably convoluted nature of the modern US pharmaceutical supply chain,[183] the difficulty in designing equitable drug pricing policies is also a factor.

---

182 Jerry Avorn. "The $2.6 Billion Pill—Methodologic and Policy Considerations." *New England Journal of Medicine* 372, 20 (2015): 1877.

183 Roshan Chikarmane, "Business Innovation: A Cure for the Drug Pricing Dilemma," Biomedical Odyssey: Life at the Johns Hopkins School of Medicine, accessed on March 15, 2020.

FORMS OF DRUG DEVELOPMENT

Broadly speaking, two approaches to drug development exist: de novo design and repurposing. De novo drug design is the creation of drugs from scratch while repurposing takes some existing drug (typically whose patent protection has expired) and finds new clinical applications for that drug. Generally, big pharma isn't bullish on repurposing drugs since expired patent protection means a lost monopoly on licensing its sale. If a pharmaceutical company has developed a molecule that is profitable, it typically doesn't want others to know what else the molecule can do. However, the National Institutes of Health (NIH) favor drug repurposing, which could be a sweet spot for AI, academia, and patients. The NIH provides grants to explore new uses of already developed drugs; according to Sem, repurposing could be a good opportunity for academia. Specifically, the National Center for Advancing Translational Sciences (NCATS) provides grants for public-private partnerships for repurposing medications.

In some sense, the barriers to drug discovery are decreasing, facilitated by the sharing of technical open-source tools that augment drug manufacture and allow computer programmers to have a more significant role in the drug discovery process. As an example, BenevolentAI has developed and made available open-source tools that aid in de novo drug development. While machine learning has been used for at least fifty years to score molecules (i.e., to predict properties given a structure), less attention has been paid to predicting structures given target properties.[184] Deep generative models

---

184 Nathan Brown et al, "GuacaMol: Benchmarking Models for de Novo Molecular Design," *Journal of Chemical Information and Modeling*

and machine learning techniques that use neural networks to produce new data objects can be applied to drug development; these techniques generate new objects, such as molecules with chemical properties like activity against a cell target.[185] These techniques are well suited for the discovery of drug candidates, which depends on evaluating how effectively a newly synthesized drug molecule will interact with its cellular targets. Guacamol, an open-source Python package developed by BenevolentAI and featured on the cover of this book, evaluates how effectively generative machine learning models can create new candidate drug molecules. Since use of neural networks in drug design is relatively new, there is a lack of consistency in evaluating how well these models are actually working— Guacamol aims to provide a standardized way of assessing new generative models for de novo molecular design.[186]

TARGET PROTEINS

Drug molecules interact with protein targets on the external side of cells. Fundamentally, this process is how drugs actually work. AI can be used to identify new protein targets to pursue, which supports both de novo drug development and repurposing. The structure of cellular proteins is complex and three-dimensional; they act as the targets for

---

59 (2019): 1096-1108.

185   Alex Zhavoronkov, et al, "Deep Learning enables rapid identification of potent DDR1 kinase inhibitors." *Nature Biotechnology* 37 (2019): 1038-1040.

186   Nathan Brown et al, "GuacaMol: Benchmarking Models for de Novo Molecular Design," *Journal of Chemical Information and Modeling* 59 (2019): 1096-1108.

drug molecules. Understanding their structure is essential to developing effective pharmaceuticals.

As a general goal for drug development, medicinal chemists need to make sense of cellular structures. So, when designing drugs, they typically first focus on protein families (e.g., kinases) and then group these protein families into subfamilies, using hidden Markov models to do so. As an example, models could be used to identify all of the dehydrogenases in the family of proteins and then develop drugs based on this process. Developing the computational models is relatively quick and led by bioinformaticists, chemists, statisticians, and now machine learning engineers. The rate-limiting process is actually designing the chemicals. In other words, the computational tools take a relatively short amount of time to develop, but actually manufacturing the chemicals in a lab takes much longer.

Markov models are used to learn how sequential data are related to each other and to perform predictions. They are a statistical tool used in weather forecasting, drug development, and, decades ago, other industries as well. One variety of Markov models is the hidden Markov model (HMM), where only certain pieces of information are known and used to predict how molecular structures interact with each other and are used in pharmacokinetics routinely and in biostatistics simulations.

MOLECULAR DOCKING

Pharmaceuticals are, after all, chemicals that are foreign to the human cell. Therefore, chemists who synthesize these molecules use techniques to determine how likely these structures are to bind to their cellular target and in what orientation. Anyone who has taken an organic chemistry class knows that chemicals exist in a variety of orientations, depending on their structure. For anyone who steered clear of organic chemistry during college, suffice it to know that drug molecules are three-dimensional and therefore can twist and turn when traveling through the bloodstream. Depending on these twists and turns of the drug molecule, it may or may not actually bind to the desired cellular target, typically an extracellular protein. Molecular docking is a computational method similar to a lock and key, where the lock is the target cellular receptor and the key is the chemical compound (or ligand) that binds to the target. Together, the receptor and drug molecule form a complex that floats in three-dimensional space within a cell.

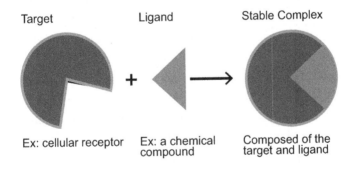

Target   Ligand   Stable Complex

Ex: cellular receptor   Ex: a chemical   Composed of the
                          compound   target and ligand

Figure 9.2: Molecular docking, whereby a drug candidate binds to a cellular receptor to form a stable complex.

Since these interactions happen in vivo, chemists need to predict how the drug molecules will bond to their intended cellular target and if their interaction will be effective. Mathematical scoring functions predict the preferred orientation of two molecules, the drug candidate and cellular receptor, in vivo. Hidden Markov models have been used to make these calculations and to score the effectiveness of the interactions.

All pharmaceutical companies have "libraries" of chemicals that are potential drug candidates. One such library is called a ZINC database, which contains hundreds of millions of compounds that can be used for drug screening. Since the scoring functions are computationally expensive and complex, AI can be used to identify the targets and match chemical libraries with proteins. Sem thinks neural networks could be used to find ways to increase the speed of docking and can scan through ZINC databases faster than traditional methods, such as force field molecular mechanics.

Machine learning tools like the ones developed at BenevolentAI are used to increase the number of candidate drugs since these tools can predict a larger pool of drug candidates than traditional methods. Though, for these techniques to be helpful, the potential efficacy of the molecules needs to be calculated reliably and systematically. Doing so entirely in a lab is costly and time consuming, and people including Zhavoronkov of Insilico Medicine are finding uses for neural networks as prefilters. For example: given ten thousand candidate structures, neural networks could predict binding affinity scores for each of the structures. In turn, this prediction can lead to a selection of a sample of candidate therapies that are most likely to succeed, decreasing the time and money of drug design and evaluation. According to Sem, large suites of data and parameters exist that could be used to build a neural network model to predict what structures will dock best.

WHAT DOES THIS ALL MEAN?

Ultimately, AI can accelerate the screening of drug candidates by detecting inactive compounds that would have failed only later, during expensive in-vivo testing. Open-source AI tools, such as the ones being developed by BenevolentAI, facilitate a democratization of drug development and will usher in a new paradigm of drug development that includes students, industry, and academia. AI will allow us to reduce the costs of drug discovery and expedite more discoveries, ultimately offering better treatment to a wider range of patients.

CHAPTER 10:

MEDICAL ADMINISTRATION AND AI

"Boring" industries benefit the most from AI.

—ANGELLIST, A STARTUP ECOSYSTEM OF
INVESTORS AND ENTREPRENEURS[187]

The US health care system has an unmistakable elephant in the room: its massive cost. The high cost of health care is driven largely by administrative complexity.[188] In the United States, administrative costs have been estimated to represent 25 to 31 percent of total health care expenditures.[189] Compared to other developed countries whose health care systems deliver good medical care, the United States typically ranks among the most expensive in the world. One recent article points how the United States spends more on health

---

187 AngelList Weekly, email message to author, October 17, 2019.

188 William Shrank, et al, "Waste in the US Health Care System Estimated Costs and Potential for Savings." *JAMA* 322, no. 15 (2019).

189 Phillip Tseng, et al, "Administrative Costs Associated with Physician Billing and Insurance-Related Activities at an Academic Health Care System." *JAMA* 319, no. 7 (2018): 691.

care than any other country, as costs approach 18 percent of the gross domestic product (GDP) and more than $10,000 per individual.[190] In a comparative study including ten other high-income countries, the United States ranks second to lowest for administrative efficiency.[191]

For context, over a hundred countries have a gross national income (GNI) per capita that is less than US per capita health care expenses. In other words, per-person health care expenses in the United States exceed per-person incomes in over a hundred of the world's countries. These countries include Brazil, Mexico, and China.

Current US GDP is estimated around $21 trillion.[192] By extension, total administrative costs of health care in the United States are an estimated $945 billion, or about $3,000 per year for every person in the country—not an insignificant amount and one that exceeds per capita GNI for at least sixty countries.

* * *

Dr. Kamal Maheshwari is an anesthesiologist at the Cleveland Clinic with a strong interest in developing AI tools to

190 William Shrank, et al, "Waste in the US Health Care System Estimated Costs and Potential for Savings." *JAMA* 322, no. 15 (2019).

191 Eric C. Schneider, et al, "Mirror, Mirror 2017: International Comparison Reflects Flaws and Opportunities for Better US Health Care," The Commonwealth Fund, accessed on September 28, 2019.

192 Report for Selected Countries and Subjects, International Monetary Fund, accessed on September 20, 2019.

improve clinical care, particularly related to perioperative care—the medical care a patient receives before, during, and after surgery. Shortly after completing his Master of Public Health from Johns Hopkins, Maheshwari began seeing opportunities for developing AI tools using historical EHR to improve care. Maheshwari has identified opportunities in two broad categories: administrative and clinical.

In the eyes of hospital decision-makers, the financial weight of administrative tasks and their repetitive nature serve as two compelling reasons to explore uses of machine learning to reduce administrative burden. The operators of hospitals, including large academic medical centers like Cleveland Clinic, evaluate their performance in multiple ways. One measure of performance is its administrative costs, which represent a significant portion of overall health care spending. Two examples of the administrative outcomes measured by hospitals are: length of stay and readmission rates. While these measures are administrative in nature, they ultimately reflect quality of care. These metrics are reported by medical centers and evaluated by hospital leadership. One component of the Affordable Care Act (ACA), the Hospital Readmissions Reduction Program (HRRP), defines financial penalties to impose on hospitals that have higher-than-expected readmission rates for targeted conditions including acute myocardial infarction, heart failure, and pneumonia.[193,194]

---

193 Hospital Readmissions Reduction Program (HRRP), Centers for Medicare and Medicaid Services, accessed on January 11, 2020.

194 Zuckerman, Rachael, et al, "Readmissions, Observation, and the Hospital Readmissions Reduction Program." *New England Journal of Medicine* 374 (2016): 1543.

These metrics are further sliced and diced by variables such as the clinical procedures performed and the attending physician. With machine learning, data analysis can quickly assess which procedures are typically associated with longer length of stay or higher readmission rates and why, thus identifying opportunities for improvements. Automated real-time analysis can also calculate performance metrics for individual physicians. Most groups have focused their work on building prediction models using machine learning for length of stay or readmission. With machine learning, algorithms are being developed to optimize administrative metrics and predict outcomes from given administrative variables. The provider has a financial incentive to keep length of stay as short as necessary while still providing good quality care and keeping readmission rates as low as possible. The quality of care is ultimately what matters, and deciding which procedures and processes are worth supporting is of immense value. For example: why maintain a process that is cheap but ineffective? On the other hand, machine learning could identify activities that are costly but result in good outcomes.

Hospitals want to avoid being identified as poor quality or an outlier on readmissions compared to peer hospitals, as well as being assessed penalties for high readmission rates. (To be fair, a financial tension exists. While hospitals are penalized for high readmissions on the state level, they generate revenue from the patient stay. This is a valid argument.) Machine learning tools can predict length of stay within the hospital given variables in the patient's record, since the machine learning tools have deciphered patterns from similar historical data. Given historical data, machine learning algorithms can predict the readmission rate for a particular combination of patient, physician, and condition. This knowledge can be used to improve care by honing clinical procedures.

The motivations for preventing hospital readmissions are well-founded. Hospital readmissions are associated with poor patient outcomes and increased expenses; they occur for almost 20 percent of patients hospitalized in the United States.[195] Typically, a readmission is defined as an inpatient stay beginning thirty days from discharge. The cause of readmission may or may not be related to the initial reason for the visit and varies across procedures. One research study that reviewed readmissions following surgery found that only 2.3 percent of patients were readmitted for the same complication they had experienced during their hospitalization, which suggests post-surgery complications as a significant driver of readmissions.[196] That particular study reported an unplanned readmission rate of 5.7 percent for nearly five hundred thousand operations. The Agency for Quality Health and Research (AQHR) estimates the following average cost of readmission, depending on the payer:[197]

- Medicare: $13,800
- Medicaid: $12,300

---

195 Stephen Jencks, et al, "Rehospitalizations among patients in the Medicare fee-for-service program," *New England Journal of Medicine* 360, no. 14(2009): 1418.

196 Ryan Merkow, et al, "Underlying Reasons Associated with Hospital Readmission Following Surgery in the United States." *JAMA.* 313, no. 5 (2015): 483.

197 Gregory Johnson, "The Cost of a US Hospital Readmission," accessed on October 20, 2019.

- Uninsured: $10,100
- Private Insurer: $14,200

Many of these readmissions are thought to be preventable.[198,199] Prior to the use of machine learning, hospitals used prediction rules to try to identify patients at greatest risk of readmission. A team of researchers at the University of Maryland developed machine learning models on a sample of over fourteen thousand patients and compared their results to those of existing prediction rules. They found their machine learning tool to be 25.5 to 54.9 percent more efficient than existing methods although they acknowledged that in practice, predicting readmissions is difficult, and intervening comes at a cost.[200] The study team used EHR data to create the predictive model. What are some possible next steps? Using this information, health plans and hospitals can design more informed policies for high-risk patients, ideally to prevent their admission in the first place.

Maheshwari has been involved with developing and evaluating machine learning tools that support perioperative care related to anesthesiology and administrative tasks. In

---

198 Medicare Payment Advisory Commission. *Report to the Congress: Promoting Greater Efficiency in Medicare.* Washington, DC: Medicare Payment Advisory Commission; 2007.

199 Andrew Auerbach, et al, "Preventability and causes of readmissions in a national cohort of general medicine patients." *JAMA Internal Medicine* 176, no. 4 (2016): 484.

200 Daniel Morgan, et al, "Assessment of Machine Learning vs Standard Prediction Rules for Predicting Hospital Readmissions." *JAMA Network Open.* 2, no. 3 (2019).

one paper, he and others applied machine learning to the manual process of assigning International Classification of Disease (ICD) codes to patient visits. ICD codes are used to categorize the nature of patient visits. While the process of assigning ICD codes to a patient visit is time-consuming and error-prone, it's an essential task for any health care provider.[201] Incorrect ICD codes lead to mistakes in billing and diagnoses—complete headaches for patients, providers, and insurers—and ultimately to worse care for the patient. Accurate machine learning tools relieve some of the burden of the manual work task of assigning or suggesting ICD codes—a process that might not appear glamorous, but one that is ripe for optimization.

* * *

Ultimately, the main source of historical data used to create administrative-related machine learning models is the EHR. Maheshwari believes the EHR is "still the largest information set about the patient," even though other sources are emerging, such as data generated from personal health devices like your FitBit or Peloton. EHR data include inpatient and outpatient details, results from laboratory tests, vital sign recordings, and diagnostics. The EHR is one of the most important and comprehensive sources of information used for machine learning models, especially for administrative machine learning models, but remember that EHRs are not perfect. Estimates suggest about 75 percent of EHR data are accurate.

---

201 Keyang Xu, et al, "Multimodal Machine Learning for Automated ICD Coding." *Proceedings of Machine Learning Research* 106 (2019): 1.

EHR systems started as a way to keep track of billing expenses, and tracking medical expenses for billing purposes was the initial purpose of ICD codes. Once early EHR systems proved themselves capable of recording billing details, new data elements were added—namely, clinical details. Early EHR systems did not contain lab results, clinical diagnoses, or research data. Centralizing billing data with clinical data allows machine learning programmers to simultaneously examine clinical outcomes and cost of service. However, none of these details could be generated without the initial patient encounter, which has led one entrepreneur to develop AI technologies to predict when patients will actually show up for their appointment.

AI APPLIED TO PATIENT SCHEDULING: MACRO-EYES

At the very core of seeing a doctor is scheduling the appointment. Nowadays, patients need to call the doctor's office or use a website or app to book an appointment. Appointment reminders are sent to the patient in a variety of ways: by email, by text, and still by mail. Despite these reminders, cancellations and rescheduling are inevitable—sometimes at the last minute and sometimes with no warning at all. No-shows and last-minute schedule changes are costly to the provider and ultimately add to the administrative costs. For a small practice, a string of cancellations can be financially disastrous.

Last-minute cancellations decrease clinical capacity, and the rescheduling of appointments is not yet automated. As a worst-case scenario, the original appointment goes unused, yet the salaried physician and their staff are still on the payroll and depend on the revenue from that lost appointment time. In an improved scenario, a secretary or even the physician work with the patient to find a better appointment time the same day. This scenario is plausible in primary care but unrealistic in many specialized areas of medicine. Last-minute changes are a headache, and filling the rescheduled spot requires a large patient population. Otherwise the original appointment slot just goes unused. As a best-case scenario, few appointments need to be rescheduled, even fewer are canceled altogether, and the provider can reliably predict the number of appointments that will be missed. Such a scenario enables the provider to plan their budget accordingly and also helps the patient since the provider will have adequate staffing and can anticipate patient needs.

* * *

Benjamin Fels is the founder and CEO of macro-eyes, a machine learning company rebuilding the foundations of health care to make the delivery of care predictive, anywhere in the world, by focusing on patient scheduling. He loves leading teams that innovate and build systems that recognize meaningful patterns. He has passion for and expertise in leading the development of predictive technology, initially in quantitative finance. As the CEO of macro-eyes, Fels has structured and successfully negotiated license and product deals with some of the largest health care organizations in the United States, which use AI tools developed by macro-eyes for predictive patient scheduling.

Even though Fels' career started in finance, he sensed a similar intensity of experience when comparing his former position in quantitative finance and his current role in health care. In both environments, he sees his role at the "front-lines of care." In quantitative finance, he managed teams that developed trading tools using data reported per second. In health care, he's developing tools that operate at the front desk of medical care—scheduling the appointment. His interest in health care stems partly from a view that as an industry, health care has incredibly rich data, yet it is "doing the least with their data." According to Fels, pattern recognition at scale is absent from the care of delivery, and that granular data about our health is typically only viewed by a small number of providers in passing. As a global industry, health care maintains and collects these granular data but is still in the process of understanding how to use these data for personalized treatment. Fels saw a disconnect and an opportunity.

Fels' team realizes that everything that happens inside the walls of the hospital depends on bringing patients into the health care system effectively through the scheduling of appointments. Yet this process can at times be inefficient and wasteful. On one hand, hospitals have valuable resources that are not being used when appointments are missed or when the demand for physicians is miscalculated. On the other hand, wait times to see a physician in hospitals are long.

When faced with a wait time of months, some patients just give up. Some might say: "I have to wait nine months? Well, I'm just gonna forget about it." The longer people have to wait to access care, the more severe the clinical problem becomes. Every year, according to Fels, the length of time for a patient to see the physician has increased. A 2017 survey reports that patients in the United States wait an average of twenty-four days to schedule an appointment with a physician.[202]

Bottlenecks in scheduling matter from a revenue perspective too. Hospitals are not paid for missed appointments. Inefficiencies in scheduling directly impact the clinical floor. Administrators and shift managers ask themselves: How many nurses do I need to have on staff on Wednesday? How many doses of X medication do I need to have? How many syringes do I need to order? If hospitals cannot accurately forecast utilization of supplies and staff, health care providers have no way to define their response, which leads to habitual over- or undersupply. This practice is incredibly expensive.

According to a McKinsey study, many health care institutions were running at around 70 percent capacity. Given his experience outside of health care, Fels reflects, "I can't think of an industry where they're running at 70 percent capacity and that's acceptable." Among the main reasons for running below capacity are habitual unexpected cancellations or planned decreased capacity to account for swells in demand. Either reason represents inefficiency, which is ultimately passed down to the patient in the form of more expensive medical care. Fels surmised that an inability to accurately forecast patient demand was the root cause for these inefficiencies; he views ensuring accurate patient scheduling as "an opportunity to make the delivery of care on the one hand predicted, which is where health care has to go, and to actually make a change in how health care operates in a way that is possible."

---

202 Bruce Japsen, "Doctor Wait Times Soar 30% in Major US Cities," Forbes, accessed on November 2, 2019.

* * *

On the trading floor, Fels was no stranger to diverse datasets. In quantitative finance, these data sources are often called "alternative data" and include things like geolocation and weather—essentially, datasets that are considered nonstandard when evaluating a company's balance sheet. Their use has grown tremendously by hedge funds over the past few years.[203] Some successful hedge fund strategies use pedestrian traffic data outside of a flagship store as a proxy for consumer demand, for example. While health care is a completely different domain, analogs to "alternative data" in health care exist. For Fels, health care data that inform predictive scheduling include socioeconomic, geographic, financial, clinical procedures, blood test results, ICD codes, unstructured text, and demographic data.

To Fels, being able to analyze all types of data is imperative. The variety of data "help us to understand that patient at this moment in time, walk through the door and predict what's likely to happen next." In other words, the programs developed at macro-eyes systematically predict the next steps of the patient, such as when they will need to schedule their follow-up appointment, and optimize for those next steps by informing the provider. Fels' team even extracts satellite imagery data to describe the environment surrounding health facilities and uses other available data to get as much context of the patient environment as possible. They use deep learning on features from satellite imagery and patient zip

---

203 "The world's most powerful data lives on Quandl," Quandl, accessed on September 1, 2019.

codes (as available), and create the more explainable models that drive Sibyl.

The flagship tool developed by macro-eyes is Sibyl, which uses a combination of traditional and alternative data to predict patient scheduling. The AI at the core of Sibyl is driving a global effort to make scheduling visits more efficient, to render the delivery of care predictive, and to better match clinical need with the right health resources at the right time. Fels and his team see scheduling as a vehicle for improving access to care. With machine learning algorithms, Sibyl predicts when each patient is most likely to show up for care and uses this insight to build more efficient operations in real time. In other words, using Sibyl, a hospital administrator will have accurate, real-time insight into the likelihood of a patient showing up for their appointment, and physicians will have a real-time aid that predicts when the patient will next need to receive care. Sibyl makes it possible for providers to see more patients, predictably and without adding clinical hours to their day.[204]

Fels' goal is to predict when you as a patient are more likely to show up for a specific appointment. In other words, he wants to ensure that exactly one patient shows up for every slot appointment. Even though Sibyl is still in early development, they are delivering 0.96 patients for every available slot, with half of the standard deviation of legacy scheduling systems. Fels cautions that Sibyl is still early in development; they are continuing to collect patient data to tell a complete story. In addition to US hospitals, they are in conversations with

204 Go Sibyl, accessed on January 11, 2020.

hospitals in Chile, India, and Mexico, which are facing the same inefficiencies in patient scheduling. Sibyl is currently used at Arkansas Heart Hospital.

While patient scheduling may seem quotidian, Fels sees the tool as addressing the $150 billion crisis in access to care. Even though Sibyl is a new tool, the applications of Sibyl reach into the areas of transforming clinical trials in the United States and designing a predictive supply chain for health. Clearly, increasing utilization of clinical resources in large hospitals is necessary. Predicable patient schedules enable providers to deal with larger numbers of patients more efficiently and anticipate supply chain needs, ultimately leading to shorter wait times and lower costs for the patient.

CHAPTER 11:

A CULTURE OF CREATION

The future of AI is here and only limited by one's imagination and energies to produce a better tomorrow.

— JIM LIEW, ENTREPRENEUR, AI EXPERT AND
ASSOCIATE PROFESSOR AT JOHNS HOPKINS[205]

Is there a recipe to success for AI in healthcare? The answer you get may depend on who you ask, but most can agree that there are always some common ingredients to success in AI. Surprisingly most of which can be found in academia. Things like capital, grit, optimism, vision, champions, adaptability, and a willingness to pivot are all necessary ingredients to a successful AI health care venture or idea. When applied inside the right culture and with the guidance and mentoring from effective leadership, great things can happen.

The environment of academic research fosters an ethos that applauds the creation of new ideas. Mark Cochran, who we learned about in earlier chapters and who has evaluated ideas in academic and commercial environments, views

---

205 "Online map tracks drive-through COVID-19 testing sites across the U.S." Johns Hopkins University Hub, accessed May 1, 2020.

universities as hypothesis machines. He has observed that innovation largely has its roots in universities and academia. To be clear, academic research is not low-stress and without risks, and securing funding to support academic research has grown increasingly competitive. Academic research is largely supported by federal grants, and the process of applying for grants is typically laborious. (One notable exception emerged during the wake of the COVID-19 pandemic in the form of privately-funded grants of $10,000 to $500,000, awarded in under 48 hours to support research related to COVID-19.[206]) Certain elements of academia nurture intellectual exploration and critical questions.

* * *

Jim Potter, who we learned about in previous chapters, is an anomaly in the field of world-class academic medical research. He has earned over forty years of continuous NIH funding at Johns Hopkins as a co-investigator or co-principal investigator—astonishing for someone who does not have a PhD or MD. He nurtures the stimulating, competitive, and high-yielding environment needed to support medical research that impacts and improves clinical care. He has mentored many medical directors and full professors and was awarded the highly regarded David M. Levine Excellence in Mentoring Award from Johns Hopkins in 2010. Although not involved with their isolation, Potter is a go-to person for questions on HeLa cells and the growth of the bioethics surrounding Henrietta Lacks.

---

206 "Fast Funding for COVID-19 Science." Fast Grants, accessed May 1, 2020.

As a mentor, Potter keeps an open-door policy for his office and exudes passion for scientific discovery and technology as well as a joy of helping students and junior colleagues. During my early days at Johns Hopkins, I recall introducing myself to a colleague as someone who works for Potter and was quickly and politely corrected by Potter, who rephrased the introduction, saying I didn't work *for* Potter, but rather *with* Potter. Not to obsess over semantics, but the minor correction set the tone for a productive and mutually respectful relationship, and is emblematic of the meaningful relationships fostered by supervisors and advisers, which can resemble a partnership.

One lesson I learned from Potter that is vital to progress in academic research and to the development of health care AI software is the idea of not becoming dependent on any single software tool. In other words, avoid falling in love with the software and instead strive to simply identify the best solution for the questions at hand.

Potter and I evaluated an open-source biobank management software application for the gastroenterology division of the Johns Hopkins University School of Medicine to determine if it could serve the biospecimen research needs of the large clinical division. Gastroenterology was a good fit for the software since biopsy specimens are collected every day from surgical endoscopy suites and used for research after study patients are properly consented. Not all clinical divisions have such high throughput access to biospecimens. In the absence of a robust software application to track collection, processing, and storage of biospecimen, researchers might use spreadsheets and locally hosted databases to store biospecimen and research participant information. While these relatively basic methods are functional for some aspects of data collection, they do not interface with the EHR and do not facilitate secure sharing of research and clinical data between collaborating labs.

Compared to proprietary software applications, the open-source software we evaluated was attractive due to its lower cost and its query capability. Open-source software is customizable, and the user benefits by having a copy of the source code, to ensure long-term viability and support of the software. By nature, software that is open-source means the code is available to anyone to view and modify, which differs from proprietary software only accessible to the vendor. Generally, Potter prefers the open-source approach and believes that "Open-source allows you to control your destiny." In other words, software development with open-source tools is less restrictive than with proprietary options.

Contributions to open-source software manifest in many forms, and the act of contributing to the software fosters collaboration and builds new relationships. Early in the pilot evaluation of the open-source biobanking software, Potter and I contributed to the open-source community by identifying bugs and potential enhancements. Users at other institutions contributed to the software by developing new features for the biobanking application and sharing the new code with the community of users. Some of these features enabled the biobanking software to integrate with clinical systems, such as the EHR system.

As I learned more about the software, I became its subject matter expert, working closely with labs that were collecting biospecimens as part of their clinical trials and research. I continued to report bugs and propose potential enhancements. In 2013, we hosted an annual conference for the open-source software, which bolstered its use at Johns Hopkins and encouraged other academic medical centers to become involved with its development. In the following years, our fellow open-source collaborators at other academic medical centers hosted similar conferences to share use cases and develop potential new features.

Initial adoption of the software focused primarily on determining usability. Reporting bugs and proposing possible enhancements were natural parts of the progression of software adoption. Improvements were driven by input from our users, who were various research labs using the software or interested in learning more. Specifically, it was valuable for the researcher to find specimens associated with a particular phenotype, which in this case means physical and pathology details that describe the specimen. We configured the application to annotate the surgical pathology diagnosis to the specimen, so a researcher could search for specimens with various grades of IBD and other phenotypic information. This feature may seem simple, but it holds significant value for the researcher, who can securely and quickly search an application for available specimens of a particular phenotype.

Given the open-source nature of the application, an interface was built to communicate between the biobanking application and the EHR system. As a possible use case: a physician with access to the biospecimen software application could determine if their patients have tissue biopsies or blood samples available for research purposes. Once the specimens are found within the system, the researcher could contact the lab who collected the specimens to ask permission to use the specimens. To use the specimens, a researcher needs IRB approval.

Potter has described biospecimens as an early form of data, saying that today's labs are yesterday's biomarkers. After all, cells have a biological story to tell. Those stories are written in genomic code, which drives protein expression and ultimately cellular function. That code is influenced by external factors, like nutrition and family history. External factors, including environment and emotion, can provoke mutations and modulate genetic switches that drive protein expression. When these external factors are carefully annotated to the biospecimen, the combination of biospecimens and patient-specific medical history becomes a very valuable dataset. Each specimen—tissue, blood, saliva, even fecal matter—contains genomic information that can be sequenced, analyzed, and stored in databases for use in machine learning tools. Biomarkers are identified and analyzed in proteomics research, and their quantification is heavily dependent on the conditions under which the specimens were collected.

OPEN-MINDED, SOMETIMES DIVERGENT

Just like the successful boxer who balances high-stakes competition with a low-pressure mindset, the developers of health care AI tools straddle a similar terrain. What does this competition look like? For one, securing grant funding in the United States is exceptionally competitive, and once the grant is awarded, the race is on.

The federal government awards around $800 billion in federal grants every year, and the NIH invests around $40 billion annually in medical research.[207] For Potter and for Hopkins Conte Digestive Diseases Center Director Mark Donowitz, the grant-writing process begins one year before the grant submission is due. For Center grants, such as the one supporting Potter, Donowitz, and about thirty other researchers, the completed grant application easily reaches a thousand pages. While the actual grant proposal is subject to character and page limitations, supporting materials such as appendices, biographies of investigators, and publications supported by prior grants add to the total length. Once the grant is awarded, recipients like Potter and Donowitz need to submit periodic progress reports to their grantor. The story is similar for any grant-funded academic medical researcher, especially for large research groups.

Grants and contracts are two very different funding mechanisms, and the nature of grants lends itself to exploratory tasks. When a contract is awarded, the recipient needs to deliver a specifically defined product in a specified period of time. When a grant is awarded, the recipient needs to carry out the work of the grant (say, develop a predictive tool to identify breast cancer) but has no guarantee that the work of the grant will deliver the specific product or accomplish its goals. And an unexpected result does not mean the grant failed. Sometimes knowing that an approach doesn't work is as valuable as knowing some approach does work. The nature of the academic environment allows for creative license, yet

207 "Research for the People," National Institutes of Health, US Department of Health and Human Services, accessed on February 20, 2020.

researchers face the constant need to secure the next round of funding, so to speak.

Grant-funded research labs aren't the only place where this creative, competitive environment is fostered. Venture capital-funded startups and early-stage companies embrace a similar ethos. The esteemed and pioneering startup incubator Y Combinator provides an environment in which entrepreneurs interact with established VCs and founders, getting iterative feedback on their products and ideas. At Y Combinator, some of this feedback is provided over a weekly dinner.[208] Picture a college student or recent graduate with a great idea, discussing API development and business strategy with VCs who broker billion-dollar deals. Universities are copying this model. FastForward is an incubator of Johns Hopkins that provides access to mentorship and funding in similar ways, often in low-stress and relaxed environments. In return, these incubators receive some percentage of equity of the technology being developed or licensed.

Multiple health care AI companies have been nurtured by the mentorship and guidance from Y Combinator alone.[209] Bot MD is a virtual assistant driven by artificial intelligence that allows the physician to quickly search for clinical protocols and for personnel, such as the contact information for attending physicians. Ian Mathews, an ER physician with the National University Health System in Singapore, has used Bot

208 "What Happens at Y Combinator," Y Combinator, accessed on September 2, 2019.

209 "YC Companies: Health Care," Y Combinator, accessed on July 11, 2019.

MD to review doses and hospital-specific protocols for using a chest tube to treat pneumothorax and to quickly look up the contact information for the senior surgical resident on call. The quick search results allow Dr. Mathews more time to focus on patients, rather than use web searches and hospital internet on his desktop.[210] Another group, Biobot, cofounded by MIT graduate Mariana Matus, analyzes city sewage to estimate opioid consumption, to inform public health action and evaluate the effectiveness of programming.[211] Biobot has found a market opportunity for its analytics and a social need, given the severity of the opioid crisis in the United States.

In some ways, the idea of technology incubators is not new. Significant technological strides were made in the 1940s, '50s, and '60s. Outside of academia, IBM and Bell Labs were bastions of innovation. Bell Labs was home to advances in secure speech devices during World War II, which were developed by Alan Turing and others. In the 1950s at IBM, computer programmer Arthur Samuel wrote the first game-playing program for checkers. Today, academia and industry are continuing to nurture creativity in technology. Academic medical centers and incubators that support early-stage and startup companies are embracing an environment that has access to funding and seasoned mentorship. Combined with access to clinical settings and guidance, these environments and their structures are propelling development of new health care AI tools.

---

210 "YC Companies: Artificial Intelligence," Y Combinator, accessed on July 11, 2019.

211 Rachel Kaufman, "Sewage May Hold the Key to Tracking Opioid Abuse," Smithsonian Magazine, August 22, 2018.

TOOLS AND CONTRIBUTORS THAT HAVE EMERGED

Many of the examples described in the book so far originated in academia. As we've seen, implementing those ideas on a large scale typically requires partnership with industry and external funding. Yoky Matsuoka, who has led projects at Google Health, began her career at MIT developing prostheses, which at the time was inspired by her desire to create a robotic tennis-playing partner. We met one of the beneficiaries of intelligent prostheses developed in the lab of Hugh Herr at MIT Media Lab. The digital pathology company Proscia was inspired by David West's interaction with established pathologists and computer scientists while he was a student at Johns Hopkins. We can observe a trend here. Many impactful health care AI ideas that straddle the riverbanks of chaos and order originate in academia. What are some of the mechanisms that bring these ideas to actual patients?

From the perspective of funding, we've seen that some initial capital is needed to get the idea off the ground and to support some of the creative, intellectual space needed to develop the idea. We saw some of this workflow outlined in chapter 3. At Johns Hopkins, the FastForward incubator has created sixteen new startups and raised $525 million in venture funding in 2019 alone.[212] FastForward's portfolio of startups includes health care AI companies, such as Bullfrog AI, which developed a precision medicine tool using artificial intelligence, to help pharmaceutical companies predict which patients will respond to treatment

212 "Programs and Services: FastForward." Johns Hopkins Technology Ventures, accessed on September 7, 2019.

in development.[213] Many founders and staff of companies supported by FastForward have some connection to Johns Hopkins—either as former students or staff—including Bullfrog AI.

At Y Combinator, over two thousand startups have been funded since 2005, the companies it has funded are now cumulatively worth over $100 billion, and over fifty thousand jobs have been created from these companies.[214] Another health care AI company supported by Y Combinator is Reverie Labs, which is building a pharmaceutical company using machine learning and focusing on cancer therapies.[215,216] Reverie Labs was founded in 2017.

Most incubators follow the model of offering mentorship, some financial capital, and sometimes physical office space. By gathering experts, funding, and ambitious entrepreneurs, they create a competitive, creative environment similar to academia, where entrepreneurs can explore ideas in a space that encourages exploration of new ideas that might fail and require frequent iteration.

---

213 "Making the Leap to Precision Medicine," Bullfrog AI: Precision Pharma, accessed on January 8, 2020.

214 "Y Combinator created a new model for funding early stage startups," Y Combinator, July 21, 2019.

215 "YC Companies: Artificial Intelligence," Y Combinator, accessed on July 11, 2019.

216 "Engineering next-generation, brain-penetrant cancer therapies," Reverie Labs, accessed on September 29, 2019.

OUTLIERS—GREG BROCKMAN, DANIEL BOURKE, BUCK'S

Not all great health care AI ideas follow the path from academic research labs to incubators to market. Greg Brockman, mentioned earlier in the book, and Daniel Bourke are two exceptions. And sometimes intangible factors act as catalysts for fruitful introductions.

Greg Brockman has been named among the list of 35 Innovators Under 35 by MIT Technology Review and cofounded OpenAI with Elon Musk and others, yet he dropped out of Harvard before finishing his degree to join Patrick Collison in the early days of Stripe. Brockman's sheer desire to build things outweighed completion of his degree. Daniel Bourke's motivations were not dissimilar. He forged his path into AI by self-creating an AI master's degree, by assembling available books and resources online through self-directed learning.[217] Having previously studied food science and nutrition, Bourke is combining his passions for AI and fitness. Many examples of nontraditional career paths exist in the field of AI.

When I interviewed Mark Cochran, we discussed some of the differences between Silicon Valley and Baltimore. A long-debated question: Why isn't the Baltimore/DC area of the country not at the top of the list of places to launch a startup? After all, companies, especially in the health care space, have many reasons to be here—access to great universities, the NIH, FDA, and exceptional labs, to name a few.

---

217 Daniel Bourke, "My Self-Created Artificial Intelligence Masters Degree," accessed on September 19, 2019.

The area is composed of whole cities of skilled practitioners and is a critical mass of expertise. Cochran offers one answer: access to risk capital. Cochran recalls that almost all of his venture investments involved firms in Palo Alto. Some firms wouldn't consider investment in companies outside of their zip code. Perhaps this fact demonstrates that even venture capital firms with plenty of risk capital are still risk-averse to a degree by minimizing their exposure to startups outside of their geographic comfort zone.

In Silicon Valley, Cochran recalls the Buck's of Woodside restaurant located near Sand Hill Road, which is known for its concentration of venture capital firms. Cochran observed Buck's as a mill for generating interactions between entrepreneurs and investors and as an open place where an entrepreneur could literally see (and engage with) the landscape of investors and competition while sitting down for pancakes. Likely many other similar environments foster dialogue between entrepreneurs and sources of risk capital. The Baltimore/DC area lacks a Buck's. The region also needs a few big successes. Silicon Valley has had many successful ventures, such as Genentech, which created new generations of investors. As founders and early investors became suddenly independently wealthy, the region began to support an unending stream of talented and smart entrepreneurs.

Exceptional health care AI ideas begin with a spark. In the right environments that allow space for thought and have good access to risk capital, the ideas can flourish. Meanwhile, there's no one definitive pathway to brilliance or excellence. The "mad scientist" who embraces irreverence and the esoteric may provides wild, new discoveries, while someone who follows a more routine, balanced strategy may have similar outcomes. To be fair, and we've seen in previous chapters, the implementation of new ideas of AI in healthcare requires adherence to ethical and legal boundaries. Perhaps the one thread that brings Brockman, West, and Bourke together is their curiosity, energy, and willingness to accept risk, even though their formal education radically differs.

CHAPTER 12:

CONCLUSION

The revolution hasn't happened yet.

—MICHAEL I. JORDAN, AMAZON SCHOLAR, AI
EXPERT, AND PROFESSOR AT UC–BERKELEY[218]

Even the pioneers of AI from the 1950s—Alan Turing, John McCarty, and Arthur Lee Samuel—could likely not have foreseen the far-reaching extensions of their work to the health care domain or envisioned the complicated ethical and legal issues that have surfaced. We are at a time in history when the computation power has begun to catch up with the ideas generated in the corridors of academic research labs and in the minds of inspired students turned entrepreneurs like David West.

As we have seen, there are critical opportunities where embracing AI can lead to better health outcomes, and many of these opportunities are already underway and have proved profitable and effective in improving the standard of care. To be sure, AI cannot simply be sprinkled onto any health

---

218 Michael I. Jordan, "Artificial Intelligence—The revolution hasn't happened yet," Amazon Science, accessed on November 25, 2019.

problem; rather, any solution relies on efforts from individuals and groups who can judiciously apply their understanding of AI and of the health domain.

In terms of health care AI tools, many approaches remain untested. More broadly, as Andrew Ng pointed out on January 1, 2020, via Twitter, the field of AI has progressed from niche to mainstream in the past decade. The technology community is just beginning to respond to meaningful use cases in health care, and the medical community is just beginning to identify cogent problem areas that can be addressed by AI technology in ways that are valuable to the patient and adhere to ethical standards. These ethical standards are still in development and continue to evolve. Medical advances have already occurred, as evidenced by multiple digital pathology startups spun out of competitive research labs, and multiple groups are pursuing open-source approaches to drug discovery, potentially decreasing the timeline of drug development in half. Regulatory processes governing drug development are adapting accordingly.

That said, as we move forward, we shouldn't expect that the process will go smoothly. Mistakes will be made. Significant advancements in technologies applied to health care will take time. Yoky Matsuoka agrees, and thinks we're going to fail a lot,[219] which is okay, and that leaders in the field will exist as a tripod of sorts—an interplay between tech companies, hospitals, and payers.[220] In order to make advancements in the

---

219 Lori Sherer, "Yoky Matsuoka of Google Health on the Future of Healthcare," Bain and Company, accessed on July 6, 2019.

220 Ibid.

field, Matsuoka thinks we have to experiment, and to have a safety net—not punish—those who are failing, to encourage those who want to try new ideas.[221]

One can easily get caught up in the hype and momentum of machine learning, so both having a cautious eye and applying the technologies in the right ways are critical. For Matsuoka and others, that means thinking first about the problem and then about the solution. After all, all the applications and algorithms related to AI are simply tools used to address some clinical problem. In the field of AI, it's easy to become enamored and excited about some technology, sometimes at the risk of losing sight of the problem that needs to be solved.

College students and recent graduates, like Karen Ayoub from New Jersey Institute of Technology, are inspired by their courses and internships and believe there's significant potential to develop AI-assisted technologies that help the patient. Ayoub is particularly interested in AI-assisted robotics for surgeries. She also sees opportunity in applying AI tools in less advanced and rural settings. Tools developed in universities and well-funded companies are poised to fill resource gaps in locations lacking staff and equipment, as we saw in the computer vision developed by Helleringer and others. Students and young people all over the world are creating advanced and impressive prototypes and contribute to the quickly evolving field of health AI. For this new generation, AI is not an abstract concept restricted to cinematic robot apocalypses (although the existential concerns voiced by Elon Musk and others over General AI have merit). Talented

221 Ibid.

students like Ayoub understand that AI can improve the day-to-day workings of many industries, including health care, to improve the patient experience.

Obstacles to implement health care AI tools exist too. We learned from Dr. Robert Miller that at least three general barriers stand in the way:

1. Making sure you have adequate tools.
2. The problem of people not trusting the system if they have spurious errors.
3. How to integrate the AI tool so it becomes useful—i.e., how do you use the tool for managing the patient, logistics, and system design?

We learned from Dr. Kamal Maheshwari that some additional barriers stem from the trust established between the patient and their physician. Maheshwari recognizes that the patient generally trusts their clinician and believes they are on their side; effectively, the patient is outsourcing their clinical decision-making to their physician. This bond needs to be maintained, and any use of AI tools should support this bond. When using a new technology to augment and enhance the physician's ability to make clinical decisions, the technology should ultimately make the patient's life easier. Perhaps a good litmus test for any machine learning intervention could be: Is the technology making the patient's life easier? Another component to this litmus test is the consideration of costs. Maheshwari points out that patients are generally very cost-sensitive. A possible addition to the litmus test: Is the technology adding costs, indirectly or directly? If so, the intervention probably won't be received well by any of the stakeholders identified in Matsuoka's tripod: technology companies, hospitals, and payers.

One of the challenges identified by Maheshwari and team was the idea that some of the machine learning models deployed in health care settings are known as "black-box" models. Such models include things like neural networks and some of the text mining techniques used in the team's research. Use of "black-box machine learning models is not convincing for physicians and insurance companies." In other words, people don't trust what they don't understand, and rightfully so. Maheshwari adds that if the technology is not able to tell us why, it's a wasteful model for us. It would be helpful for the tool to report, "This prediction was made, and it was determined by these 1, 2, 3 factors." This approach and mindset align with some of the principles set forth in Google's documentation on explainable AI. With neural networks and some black-box algorithms, sometimes it is just not possible to report the exact features that determine a decision. A central question for the field becomes: Should we restrict the models used in health care to only models that have clear determinants and therefore can be easily explained and understood?

Currently, the process of training machine learning models and deciding which model to use is not straightforward. Some optimism can be found from experts and teachers like Josh Gordon, who travels to teach people about the machine learning tools being developed at Google. Gordon reminds programmers to continue to work on hard problems—even though the payoff is distant, or uncertain—and that without any risk, you get no reward. Despite initial challenges common to any machine learning problem, Gordon thinks anyone can learn machine learning, and it's easier than one might think. As we've learned, established physicians like Dr. Robert Miller are cautious of tools developed by people with incomplete knowledge of the mathematics responsible for machine learning models, but perhaps an entry-level knowledge of machine learning models will be helpful—if not necessary—for more trusted adoption of health care AI tools by those receiving care.

Data ownership and appropriate sharing of data are closely related challenges in the development of machine learning models within health care. Ultimately, patients are the primary source of data for health care models, whether the data originate from EHRs, medical devices, wearable devices, or personal diagnostic tests like 23andMe. Patients need to be informed of potential downstream uses of their data at the time of data collection, which could be accomplished through use of broad consents or perhaps by some other novel mechanism not yet developed. Currently, some of the commercial data agreements allow the collector of data to perform analysis on the data and share the data with third parties.

The development and implementation of health care AI tools are opening the doors to new ethical and legal challenges. Use of the data by the collector can lead to profitable outcomes, which typically are not returned to patients, but rather retained by the collector of data or a third party. This flow of data is ripe for ethical and legal questions, such as:[222]

222 "I. Glenn Cohen - AI in Healthcare: Legal and Ethical Issues," Harvard Global Health Institute, accessed on July 25, 2019.

1. To what degree should patients be involved in deciding what happens with their data?
2. Do patients have the necessary voice when deciding what happens with their data?
3. How do we create data governance models that protect the patient and facilitate innovation?
4. Could data governance resemble a union: a union of patients who control over their data, or maybe a trust with a fiduciary?

We can see several examples where issues of data ownership lead to trouble for the data collector. As evidenced by a recent lawsuit based on allegations that the University of Chicago shared their electronic health records with Google without asking individual patients one by one, patients become upset when they find out their EHR data are possibly being used without their express permission.[223] So, while the most effective machine learning algorithms require as much training data as possible, a real tension exists between ensuring patient data privacy and building training set data that are large and also diverse.[224] These disputes arise from ambiguity in ownership of data. Do the data belong to the patient? Do the data belong to the data collector (such as the hospital or company)? What constitutes an official transfer of ownership, and under which circumstances is it necessary to obtain consent to transfer health data?

---

223 I. Glenn Cohen, "Ethics & the Law – I. Glenn Cohen, Professor of Law at Harvard University – Technology, Law, Ethics, and What's on the Horizon." August 20, 2019, in *Finding Genius Podcast Future Tech Edition*, produced by Richard Jacobs, podcast, 35:44.

224 Ibid.

DR. ROBERT MILLER

Dr. Miller believes it is worrisome, if not unethical, to be dependent on algorithms that sometimes produce undetectable errors. He thinks ultimately AI technology will not replace the skills of domain experts, such as pathologists and other medical specialties, but we might use machine learning to assist them. Dr. Miller offers the following example: handheld calculators are used to perform things like long division and exponents—things that many of us learned in elementary or middle school but have since forgotten how to perform or that just take too long for us to do with paper and pencil. Will the medical field have analogous machine learning tools that serve as calculators too? What are the long division and exponent equivalents of machine learning? Even as calculators are used as shortcuts and to facilitate routine math functions, we must all first learn the underlying math concepts before using the shortcut buttons on our calculators. In health care AI, the analogy holds true that creators of machine learning models in health care should understand the mechanics behind the algorithms used in clinical care. To some degree, the analogy holds true for users of machine learning tools. In the coming few years, we will see how (or if) the field of explainable AI promotes both caregivers' and patients' understanding of machine learning tools and fosters patient engagement.

Dr. Miller believes that the most important thing in health care AI is that we all need to learn more. We need to form diverse groups of people to learn more about how AI works. Consider the following example:

I am going for a chest x-ray that is being evaluated by four algorithms. Three of those algorithms agree with the diagnoses, but one algorithm believes we should focus on another region of the chest—and these are the reasons: x, y, and z.

In this sense, perhaps the field of explainable AI will become a strong bridge between health care providers, technical experts, and patients.

INSPIRATION

When Robert Longyear decided to go into the field of health care, he had no idea that one day his mother would be diagnosed with chronic myeloid leukemia (CML). Although he studied health care management and policy at Georgetown University and held internships at Medicaid, he would learn more about the health care system during the experience of caring for his mother than during any other part of his career.

While completing his undergraduate studies, his mother received her CML diagnosis. Longyear recalls, "In my sophomore year, I lost my mom to cancer, and in the six months before that happened, it was as though we were in and out of the hospital and taking care of her and managing her medication." He learned the difficulty of coordinating medications. He couldn't possibly imagine other people going through the same thing.

The lessons he learned while caring for his mother encouraged Longyear to improve the process of coordinating prescription medications. Before joining Montuno full time, Longyear consulted for the company's efforts to build an enterprise product for hospitals and insurers based on their mobile application, Dosecast. Dosecast is a mobile app that tracks prescription medication and allows patients to set reminders to take their medication at the appropriate time; it allows providers to manage care in real time. As it's an enterprise application, the team envisioned using the patient-facing interface of the mobile application and building a new backend dashboard to feed in real-time data and analytics from the provider. The enterprise version, the Dosecast Digital Care Management Platform, began with the idea of improving prescription drug adherence and has grown into a mobile care-management platform that connects providers, care managers, and patients.[225]

Longyear was asked to join the team full time to support product management and development of the enterprise Dosecast product and to refine Montuno's research and development strategy. Part of Montuno's strategy included development of machine learning for risk stratification. While caring for his mother, he experienced the difficulty in coordinating medications during cancer treatment, and he recalls how he "learned a lot during the process—more than I could have ever learned in school." Longyear couldn't possibly imagine other people going through the same thing with fewer resources and less health care education, which served as his inspiration to support prescription drug adherence using digital tools.

---

225 "Customers,"Montuno Software, accessed on November 5, 2019.

What kept him going during this time was the idea that he could prevent the confusion and difficulty of care management for others in similar situations. The confusion and time-consuming nature of medication coordination could have been defeating for Longyear, but he had the determination to find ways to help patients live normal lives during medical treatment. From this experience, Longyear became passionate about helping people manage medical treatment and prescription medication adherence on their own. According to Longyear, the health system is currently designed for sick care rather than preventive care that keeps patients out of facilities.

Longyear recognizes that medicine can do incredible things, especially given the research conducted in the area, but in some ways, Longyear feels the US health system is still oriented in the same way it was in the 1900s. Our health care system tends to be more complicated than a lot of industries, given the multitude of payers and mixed incentives. The system tends to be reactionary in nature. Robert sees a duty to prevent illnesses by using predictive tools to shift how health care is delivered, especially in support of preventative medicine.

The quote at the beginning of the conclusion comes from Michael Jordan, who has been named one of the most influential computer scientists of our time and is a renowned researcher in machine learning. Jordan recognizes machine learning as a branch of engineering that is humanized, meaning it will not just be built off hard numbers; he believes it will have elements of humanity to it because it will affect real lives, real people, and real problems.[226] As a society, we are just beginning to learn and address some of the emerging challenges that face applications of AI in health care. Jordan argues that whether or not we come to understand the meaning of "intelligence" any time soon, we face the challenge of bringing computers and humans together in ways that enhance human life.[227] As consumers, developers, and users of AI in health care, we too should strive to build tools that ultimately enhance human life.

226 Michael I. Jordan, "Artificial Intelligence—The revolution hasn't happened yet," Amazon Science, accessed on November 25, 2019.

227 Ibid.

APPENDIX

ACKNOWLEDGMENTS

GitHub. "guacamol/guacamol/scoring_function.py" Benevolent AI. Accessed on March 14, 2020. https://github.com/BenevolentAI/guacamol/blob/master/guacamol/scoring_function.py

CHAPTER 0: INTRODUCTION

"Business Associate Contracts." US Department of Health and Human Services. Accessed on March 31, 2020. https://www.hhs.gov/hipaa/for-professionals/covered-entities/sample-business-associate-agreement-provisions/index.html

Cuocolo, Renato, Teresa Perillo, Eliana De Rosa, Lorenzo Ugga, and Mario Petretta. "Current applications of big data and machine learning in cardiology." *Journal of Geriatric Cardiology* 16, no. 8 (2019): 601-607.

Dave, Paresh. "Google signs healthcare data and cloud computing deal with Ascension." Reuters. Accessed on November 13, 2019. https://www.reuters.com/article/us-alphabet-ascension-privacy/google-signs-healthcare-data-and-cloud-computing-deal-with-ascension-idUSKBN1XL2AT

Day, Sean. "2018 Funding Part 2: Seven more takeaways from digital health's $8.1B year." Rock Health. Accessed on

October 2, 2019. https://rockhealth.com/reports/seven-more-takeaways-from-digital-healths-8-1b-year/

"Harnessing the Power of Data in Health." Stanford Medicine 2017 University Trends Report. Stanford University. Accessed on October 3, 2019. https://med.stanford.edu/content/dam/sm/sm-news/documents/StanfordMedicineHealthTrendsWhitePaper2017.pdf

"HIPAA Privacy and Security and Workplace Wellness Programs" US Department of Health and Human Services. Accessed on March 30, 2020. https://www.hhs.gov/hipaa/for-professionals/privacy/workplace-wellness/index.html

Lazer, David. "What We Can Learn from the Epic Failure of Google Flu Trends," Wired. Accessed on March 29, 2020. https://www.wired.com/2015/10/can-learn-epic-failure-google-flu-trends/

McCarthy, Niall. "America's Most and Least Trusted Professions." Forbes. Accessed on March 31, 2020. https://www.forbes.com/sites/niallmccarthy/2019/01/11/americas-most-least-trusted-professions-infographic/#a8e97707e94e

Murgia, Madhumita. "DeepMind runs up higher losses and debts in race for AI." Financial Times. Accessed on September 12, 2019. https://www.ft.com/content/d4280856-b92d-11e9-8a88-aa6628ac896c

"President Trump's FY 2021 Budget Commits to Double Investments in Key Industries of the Future." White House press release. February 11, 2020.

Schneider, Eric, Dana Sarnak, David Squires, Arnav Shah, and Michelle Doty. "Mirror, Mirror 2017: International Comparison Reflects Flaws and Opportunities for Better US Health Care." The Commonwealth Fund. Accessed on September 28, 2019. https://www.commonwealthfund.org/publications/fund-reports/2017/jul/mirror-mirror-2017-international-comparison-reflects-flaws-and

"Soon you could visit your pharmacist instead of your primary care doctor for common ailments." News 5 Cleveland. Accessed on March 31, 2020. https://www.news5cleveland.com/news/e-team/soon-you-could-visit-your-pharmacist-instead-of-your-primary-care-doctor-for-common-ailments

Vilne, Baiba, Irena Meistere, Lelde Grantina-levina, and Juris Kibilds. "Machine Learning Approaches for Epidemiological Investigations of Food-Borne Disease Outbreaks." *Frontiers in Microbiology* 10, (2019).

Wachter, Robert. *The Digital Doctor: Hope, Hype, and Harm at the Dawn of Medicine's Computer Age.* Mc-Graw Hill Publishing. 2015.

CHAPTER 1: HISTORY OF AI

Anderson, Derek. "The story behind payment disruptor stripe.com and its founder Patrick Collison." Tech Crunch. Accessed July 20, 2019. https://techcrunch.com/2012/05/20/the-story-behind-payment-disruptor-stripe-com-and-its-founder-patrick-collison/

Brender J. Handbook of evaluation methods for health informatics. Burlington, MA: Elsevier Academic Press. 2006.

Harari, Yuval Noah. "21 Lessons for the 21st Century." Spiegel & Grau. 2018.

Jordan, Michael I. "Artificial Intelligence—The revolution hasn't happened yet." Amazon Science. Accessed on November 25, 2019. https://www.amazon.science/artificial-intelligence-the-revolution-hasnt-happened-yet

Ng, Andrew. Twitter Post. January 1, 2020, 3:23 AM. https://twitter.com/AndrewYNg/status/1212288286024065024

Petroski, Henry. "Patterns of Failure." Modern Steel Construction. July 2006.

Raschka, Sebastian. "Single-Layer Neural Networks and Gradient Descent." Accessed April 27, 2020. "https://sebastianraschka.com/Articles/2015_singlelayer_neurons.html

Samuel, Arthur. "Some Studies in Machine Learning Using the Game of Checkers." *IBM Journal of Research and Development*. 44: 206–226.

Saria, Suchi and Adarsh Subbaswamy. Tutorial: Safe and Reliable Machine Learning. In ACM Conference on Fairness, Accountability, and Transparency. 2019.

Shortliffe, Edward. "Artificial Intelligence in Medicine: Weighing the Accomplishments, Hype, and Promise." *IMIA Yearbook of Medical Informatics*, (2019): 257-62.

Sibly, Paul. "The Production of Structural Failures." PhD Thesis. University of London. 1977.

Walch, Kathleen. "Artificial Intelligence is Not a Technology." Forbes. Accessed on August 10, 2019. https://www.forbes.com/sites/cognitiveworld/2018/11/01/artificial-intelligence-is-not-a-technology/#1ad33bad5dcb

CHAPTER 2: ESSENTIAL AI AND MACHINE LEARNING CONCEPTS

"A Comparison of Chess and Go." British Go Association. Accessed on August 18, 2019. https://www.britgo.org/learners/chessgo

Ardila, Diego, Atilla Kiraly, Sujeeth Bharadwaj, Bokyung Choi, Joshua Reicher, Lily Peng, Daniel Tse, Mozziyar Etemadi, Wenxing Ye, Greg Corrado, David Naidich, Shravya Shetty. "End-to-end lung cancer screening with three-dimensional deep learning on low-dose chest computed tomography," *Nature Medicine*, 25 (2019): 954–961.

Carroll, Robert, Will Thompson, Anne Eyler, Arthur Mandelin, Tianxi Cai, Raquel Zink, Jennifer Pacheco, Chad Boomershine, Thomas Lasko, Hua Xu, Elizabeth Karlson, Raul Perez, Vivian Gainer, Shawn Murphy, Eric Ruderman, Richard Pope, Robert Plenge, Abel Kho, Katherine Liao, Joshua Denny. "Portability of an algorithm to identify rheumatoid arthritis in electronic health records." *Journal of the American Medical Informatics Association* 19 (2012): e162–e169.

Cuthbertson, Anthony. "How Artificial Intelligence is Helping Japanese Cucumber Farmers." Newsweek. Accessed on March 31, 2020. https://www.newsweek.com/artificial-intelligence-cucumber-farm-raspberry-pi-495289

Dean, Jeff. "How Will Artificial Intelligence Affect Your Life," TEDXLA. Accessed on March 31, 2020. https://www.youtube.com/watch?v=BfDQNrVphLQ

DeepMind, "AlphaGo." Accessed on October 10, 2019. https://deepmind.com/research/case-studies/alphago-the-story-so-far

Fairley, Peter. "Algorithms Help Turbines Share the Wind." IEEE Spectrum. July 1, 2019. https://spectrum.ieee.org/energy-wise/green-tech/wind/teaching-wind-turbines-wake-steering

Good Dog. "Elon Musk's Last Warning About Artificial Intelligence." September 16, 2019. Video, 23:36. https://www.youtube.com/watch?v=VIaiNK7MoX8.

Google Developers. "ML Recipe #1: Hello World." May 30, 2016. Video, 6:52. https://youtu.be/cKxRvEZd3Mw.

KMTS. "What is the EMR Mandate?" Kristin Muller Transcription. Accessed on March 31, 2020. https://kristinmullertranscription.com/what-is-the-emr-mandate/

Krizhevsky, Alex, Ilya Sutskever, and Geoffrey Hinton. "ImageNet Classification with Deep Convolutional Neural Networks." Neural Information Processing Systems.

Liao, Katherine, Tianxi Cai, Vivian Gainer, Sergey Goryachev, Qing Zeng-Treitler, Soumya Raychaudhuri, Peter Szolovits, Susanne Churchill, Shawn Murphy, Isaac Kohane, Elizabeth Karlson, and Robert Plenge. "Electronic Medical Records for Discovery Research in Rheumatoid Arthritis." *Arthritis Care & Research* 62, no. 8 (2010): 1120-1127.

Massachusetts Institute of Technology. "NLP" Accessed on March 31, 2020. https://mlhc19mit.github.io/slides/lecture7.pdf

McKinney, Scott, Marcin Sieniek, Varun Godbole, Jonathan Godwin, Natasha Antropova, Hutan Ashrafian, Trevor Back, Mary Chesus, Greg Corrado, Ara Darzi, Mozziyar Etemadi, Florencia Garcia-Vicente, Fiona Gilbert, Mark Halling-Brown, Demis Hassabis, Sunny Jansen, Alan Karthikesalingam, Christopher Kelly, Dominic King, Joseph Ledsam, David Melnick, Hormuz Mostofi, Lily Peng, Joshua Reicher, Bernardino Romera-Paredes, Richard Sidebottom, Mustafa Suleyman, Daniel Tse, Kenneth Young, Jeffrey De Fauw, and Shravya Shetty. "International evaluation of an AI system for breast cancer screening." *Nature* 755 (2020): 89-94.

"Microsoft to acquire GitHub for $7.5 billion." Microsoft News Center. Accessed on September 18, 2019. https://news.microsoft.com/2018/06/04/microsoft-to-acquire-github-for-7-5-billion/

Peng, Lily. "Deep Learning for Detection of Diabetic Eye Disease." Google AI Blog. Accessed on October 2, 2019. https://ai.googleblog.com/2016/11/deep-learning-for-detection-of-diabetic.html

Prasad, Niranjani, Li-Fang Cheng, Corey Chivers, Michael Draugelis, and Barbara Engelhardt. "A Reinforcement Learning Approach to Weaning of Mechanical Ventilation in Intensive Care Units." 2017. arXiv:1704.06300

PyTorch. "Pytorch at Tesla." November 6, 2019. Video, 11:10. https://youtu.be/oBklltKXtDE

Rajkomar, Alvin and Eyal Oren. "Deep Learning for Electronic Health Records," Google AI Blog. Accessed on March 31, 2020. https://ai.googleblog.com/2018/05/deep-learning-for-electronic-health.html

Rajkomar, Alvin, Eyal Oren, Kai Chen, Andrew Dai, Nissan Hajaj, Michaela Hardt, Peter Liu, Xiaobing Liu, Jake Marcus, Mimi Sun, Patrik Sundberg, Hector Yee, Kun Zhang, Yi Zhang, Gerardo Flores, Gavin Duggan, Jamie Irvine, Quoc Le, Kurt Litsch, Alexander Mossin, Justin Tansuwan, De Wang, James Wexler, Jimbo Wilson, Dana Ludwig, Sameul Volchenboum, Katherine Chou, Michael Pearson, Srinivasan Madabushi, Nigam Shah, Atul Butte, Michael Howell, Claire Cui, Greg Corrado, and Jeffrey Dean. "Scalable and accurate deep learning with electronic health records." *npj Digital Medicine* 1, no.18 (2018).

Sample, Ian. "AI system outperforms experts in spotting breast cancer." The Guardian. Accessed on January 10, 2020. https://www.theguardian.com/society/2020/jan/01/ai-system-outperforms-experts-in-spotting-breast-cancer

"Seeing Potential: How a team at Google is using AI to help doctors prevent blindness in diabetes." Google. Accessed on March 20, 2020. https://about.google/intl/en_us/stories/seeingpotential/

Shetty, Shravya. "A promising step forward for predicting lung cancer." Google. Accessed on June 2, 2019. https://www.blog.google/technology/health/lung-cancer-prediction/

CHAPTER 3: IDEA TO IMPLEMENTATION

Altman, Sam. "AI." Accessed on February 17, 2020. https:// blog.samaltman.com/ai

"Microsoft Power Apps on Azure." Microsoft. Accessed on March 12, 2020. https://azure.microsoft.com/en-us/products/powerapps/

Montuno Software. Accessed on October 20, 2019. https:// www.montunosoftware.com/

Patyal, Saurav. "BenevolentAI: Revolutionizing drug discovery using Artificial Intelligence." HBS Digital Initiative. Accessed on January 9, 2020. https://digital.hbs.edu/platform-digit/ submission/benevolentai-revolutionizing-drug-discovery-using-artificial-intelligence/

"People + AI Guidebook: Designing Human-Centered AI Product." PAIR with Google. Accessed on August 30, 2020. https://pair.withgoogle.com/guidebook/

Ransohoff, David and Alvan Feinstein. "Problems of Spectrum and Bias in Evaluating the Efficacy of Diagnostic Tests." *New England Journal of Medicine* 299, no.17 (1978):926-930.

"The Johns Hopkins ACG System: Decades of Impact on Population Health Research and Practice." *The Johns Hopkins University.* 2020.

CHAPTER 4: ETHICAL AI

"Belmont Report: Ethical Principles and Guidelines for the Protection of Human Subjects of Research." Department of Health, Education, and Warfare. Report of the National Commission for the Protection of Human Subjects of Biomedical and Behavioral Research.

Cohen, I. Glenn. "Ethics & the Law – I. Glenn Cohen, Professor of Law at Harvard University – Technology, Law, Ethics, and What's on the Horizon." August 20, 2019. In *Finding Genius Podcast Future Tech Edition*. Produced by Richard Jacobs. Podcast, 35:44. https://futuretech.findinggeniuspodcast.com/podcasts/ethics-the-law-i-glenn-cohen-professor-of-law-at-harvard-university-technology-law-ethics-and-whats-on-the-horizon/

Espinoza, Javier. "IBM and Microsoft sign Vatican Pledge for Ethical AI." Financial Times. Accessed on March 3, 2020. https://www.ft.com/content/5dc6edcc-5981-11ea-a528-ddof971febbc

"Faculty Directory: Stéphane Helleringer, PhD." Johns Hopkins Bloomberg School of Public Health. Accessed on August 22, 2019. https://www.jhsph.edu/faculty/directory/profile/3136/st-phane-helleringer

Fisher, Christine. "IBM and Microsoft Support the Vatican's Guidelines for Ethical AI." MSN. Accessed on March 2, 2020. https://www.msn.com/en-us/news/technology/ibm-and-microsoft-support-the-vatican-s-guidelines-for-ethical-ai/ar-BB10x9xh

"Global Projects." Johns Hopkins Bloomberg School of Public Health. Accessed on November 10, 2019. https://www.jhsph.edu/faculty/research/search/results/project/9308

Harvard Global Health Institute. "I. Glenn Cohen—AI in Healthcare: Legal and Ethical Issues." May 23, 2019. Video, 11:06. https://youtu.be/oRuL6kzg7wo

"In the Age of AI." *PBS.* Accessed on December 2, 2019. https://www.pbs.org/wgbh/frontline/film/in-the-age-of-ai/

Ledford, Heidi. "Millions of black people affected by racial bias in health-care algorithms." Nature Research Journal. October 26, 2019.

O'Neil, Cathy. *Weapons of Math Destruction.* Crown Books Publishing. p. 21, September 2016.

Obermeyer, Ziad, Brian Powers, Christine Vogeli, Sendhil Mullainathan. "Dissecting racial bias in an algorithm used to manage the health of populations." *Science* 336 no. 6464 (2019): 447–453.

Park, Alice. "Cardiologist Eric Topol on How AI Can Bring Humanity Back to Medicine." TIME Magazine. Accessed on January 11, 2020. https://time.com/5551296/cardiologist-eric-topol-artificial-intelligence-interview/

Pullella, Philip. "Pope Urges Silicon Valley to Avoid Slide Toward New 'Barbarism.'" Reuters. Accessed on October 1, 2019. https://www.reuters.com/article/us-vatican-technology-ethics/pope-urges-silicon-valley-to-avoid-slide-toward-new-barbarism-idUSKBN1WC11N

Rosso, Cami. "The Conundrum of Machine Learning and Cognitive Biases." Medium. Accessed January 10, 2020.

https://medium.com/@camirosso/the-conundrum-of-machine-learning-and-cognitive-biases-ce4b82a87f49

Sheehan, Mark. "Can Broad Consent be Informed Consent?" *Public Health Ethics* 4, no. 3 (2011): 226-235.

Stephane Helleringer. "Improving age measurement in low- and middle-income countries through computer vision: A test in Senegal." Vol. 40, Art. 9:(219-26., January 29, 2019.

Van Sant, Shannon and Richard Gonzalez. "San Francisco Approves Ban on Government's Use of Facial Recognition Technology." NPR. Accessed on August 17, 2019. https://www.npr.org/2019/05/14/723193785/san-francisco-considers-ban-on-governments-use-of-facial-recognition-technology

"World Medical Association Declaration of Helsinki." June 1964.

CHAPTER 5: REGULATORY AND LEGAL CONSIDERATIONS

Abernethy, Amy, and Vijay Pande. "Food, Drugs, and Tech—100 Years of Public Health." Andreessen Horowitz. Accessed on January 20, 2020. https://a16z.com/2020/01/06/future-of-fda-amy-abernethy/

"Beyond the HIPAA Privacy Rule: Enhancing Privacy, Improving Health Through Research." National Center for Biotechnology Information, US National Library of Medicine. 2009.

Cohen, I. Glenn, and Michelle Mello. "HIPAA and Protecting Health Information in the 21st Century." *JAMA Network.* July 17, 2018.

CMS Data. Centers for Medicare and Medicaid Services. Accessed on September 29, 2019. https://data.cms.gov/

Harvard Global Health Institute. "I. Glenn Cohen—AI in Healthcare: Legal and Ethical Issues." May 23, 2019. Video, 11:06. https://youtu.be/oRuL6kzg7wo

Hill, Kashmir. "How Target Figured Out a Teen Girl Was Pregnant before Her Father Did." Forbes. Accessed on September 3, 2019. https://www.forbes.com/sites/kashmirhill/2012/02/16/how-target-figured-out-a-teen-girl-was-pregnant-before-her-father-did/

Marcus, Julia, Leo Hurley, Douglas Krakower, Stacey Alexeeff, Michael Silverberg, Jonathan Volk. "Use of Electronic Health Record Data and Machine Learning to Identify Candidates for HIV Pre-exposure Prophylaxis: A Modelling Study." *The Lancet HIV* 6, no. 10 (2019).

Musk, Elon. Twitter Post. February 17, 2020, 6:22 PM. https://twitter.com/elonmusk/status/1229546793811226627.

Pearlman, Alex. "HIPAA Is the Tip of the Iceberg When It Comes to Privacy and Your Medical Data." Harvard Law Petrie-Flom Center. Accessed July 29, 2019. https://blog.petrieflom.law.harvard.edu/2019/01/07/hipaa-is-the-tip-of-the-iceberg-when-it-comes-to-privacy-and-your-medical-data/

Price, Nicholson W., and I. Glenn Cohen. "Privacy in the age of medical big data." *Nature Medicine* 27 (2019): 37-43.

"Proposed regulatory framework for modifications to artificial intelligence/ machine learning (AI/ML)-based software as a medical device (SaMD)." US Food & Drug Administration. 2019.

Sherer, Lori. "Yoky Matsuoka of Google Health on the Future of Health care." Bain and Company. Accessed on July 6, 2019. https://www.bain.com/insights/yoky-matsuoka-of-google-health-on-the-future-of-healthcare/

"Software as a medical device (SaMD)." US Food & Drug Administration. Accessed on January 24, 2020. https://www.fda.gov/medical-devices/digital-health/

Vincent, James. "Google accused of inappropriate access to medical data in potential class-action lawsuit." The Verge. Accessed November 2, 2019. https://www.theverge.com/2019/6/27/18760935/google-medical-data-lawsuit-university-of-chicago-2017-inappropriate-access

Wakabayashi, Daisuke. "Google and the University of Chicago Are Sued Over Data Sharing." New York Times. Accessed on August 18, 2019. https://www.nytimes.com/2019/06/26/technology/google-university-chicago-data-sharing-lawsuit.html

CHAPTER 6: INFRASTRUCTURE

"A-Level Capital." Accessed on March 31, 2020. http://www.alevelcapital.com/

"About Us: MedHacks 2020." MedHacks 2020. Accessed on March 31, 2020. https://medhacks.io

"Artificial Intelligence at Google: Our Principles." GoogleAI. Accessed on March 31, 2020. https://ai.google/principles

"Machine learning: what it is and why it matters." SAS. Accessed on March 31, 2020. https://www.sas.com/en_id/insights/analytics/machine-learning.html

"MIT Hacking Medicine." MIT Hacking Medicine. Accessed on March 31, 2020. https://hackingmedicine.mit.edu/

Shipley Wins. Accessed on July 25, 2019. https://www.shipleywins.com/about/

SiliconANGLE theCUBE. "Stanford Women in Data Science (WiDS) Conference 2020." March 2, 2020. Video, 12:22. https://youtu.be/7TlZ7loJ76o.

"Small Business Innovation Research (SBIR)." Small Business Administration. Accessed on July 9, 2019. https://www2.ed.gov/programs/sbir/index.html

Topol, Eric. "Deep Medicine: How Artificial Intelligence Can Make Healthcare Human Again." New York: Basic Books. 2019.

"Y Combinator created a new model for funding early stage startups." Y Combinator. Accessed on July 21, 2019. https://www.ycombinator.com/index.html

CHAPTER 7: MENTORSHIP, ROBOTICS, AND NEURONS

"Da Vinci Research Kit." GitHub. Accessed on January 3, 2020. https://github.com/researchkit/

"Discovering and enacting the path to safe artificial general intelligence." OpenAI. Accessed on March 31, 2020. https://openai.com/

"Dissecting the Language of Surgery." Johns Hopkins University. Accessed on January 25, 2020. https://engineering.jhu.edu/magazine/2010/01/dissecting-language-surgery/

Hirsch, Arthur. "Johns Hopkins scientist programs robot to perform 'soft tissue' surgery." Johns Hopkins University. Accessed on January 4, 2020. https://hub.jhu.edu/2016/05/06/robot-soft-tissue-surgery/

Horvitz, Eric. "AI and Our Future with Machines with Dr. Eric Horvitz." December 4, 2017. In *Microsoft Research Podcast*. Podcast, 26:12. https://www.microsoft.com/en-us/research/blog/ai-and-our-future-with-machines-eric-horvitz/

"Making Friends With Artificial Intelligence: Eric Horvitz at TEDxAustin." TEDxAustin. Accessed on September 29, 2019. https://youtu.be/dpoVh9xwdD4

Nadella, Satya. "Can Microsoft's chief Satya Nadella restore it to glory?" Financial Times. October 13, 2017.

"OpenAI." GitHub. Accessed on March 31, 2020. https://github.com/openai

"Overview: Robotic Surgery." Mayo Foundation for Medical Education and Research. Accessed January 10, 2020. https://www.mayoclinic.org/tests-procedures/robotic-surgery/about/pac-20394974

"Pairing human ingenuity with technology." Intuitive. Accessed on October 29, 2019. https://www.intuitive.com/en-us/about-us/company

"Robotic Prostatectomy." Johns Hopkins Medicine. Accessed on January 22, 2020. https://www.hopkinsmedicine.org/health/treatment-tests-and-therapies/robotic-prostatectomy

Schulman, John, Ankush Gupta, Sibi Venkatesan, Mallory Tayson-Frederick, Pieter Abbeel. "A Case Study of Trajectory Transfer Through Non-Rigid Registration for a Simplified Suturing Scenario." Berkeley University.

"The dVRK Allows Worldwide Research in Robotic Surgery." Laboratory for Computational Sensing and Robotics. Johns Hopkins University. Accessed on January 15, 2020. https://lcsr.jhu.edu/2017/02/08/dvrk-research-robotic-surgery/

Trafton, Anne. "New method visualizes groups of neurons as they compute." MIT Media Lab via MIT News. October 9, 2019.

Waters, Richard. "Microsoft invests $1bn in OpenAI effort to replicate human brain." Financial Times. July 22, 2019.

CHAPTER 8: A LEG UP: PATHOLOGY AND PROSTHESES

"3-D Printed Prosthetic Hand Fit for a Superhero." As seen in the 2016 Biennial Report, Johns Hopkins University. Accessed on September 7, 2019. https://www.hopkinsmedicine.org/news/stories/3d_griffin.html

Comstock, Jonah. "Digital pathology startup Deep Lens raises $3.2M." MobiHealthNews. Accessed on August 12, 2019.

https://www.mobihealthnews.com/content/digital-patholo-gy-startup-deep-lens-raises-32m

"E-nable Is Growing." Enabling the Future. Accessed on August 12, 2019. http://enablingthefuture.org/

Freitas, Tiffany. "PathAI Secures $60M in Series B Funding Led by General Atlantic and Existing Investor General Catalyst." Businesswire. April 17, 2019.

Hale, Conor. "MSKCC-backed digital pathology startup nets FDA breakthrough device designation." FierceBiotech. March 7, 2019.

"How AI is helping patients with prosthetics." Today. September 30, 2019.

Herr, Hugh. "How we'll become cyborgs and extend human potential," TED. Accessed on July 19, 2019. https://www.ted.com/talks/hugh_herr_how_we_ll_become_cyborgs_and_extend_human_potential.

Lunden, Ingrid. "PaigeAI nabs $25M, inks IP deal with Sloan Kettering to bring machine learning to cancer pathology." TechCrunch. February 5, 2018.

"Matching the right patient with the right trial at the right time" Deep Lens. Accessed on July 10, 2019. https://www.deeplens.ai/

Molteni, Megan. "Want a True Bionic Limb? Good Luck Without Machine Learning." Wired. May 3, 2017.

Mone, Amy. "Johns Hopkins cancer pioneer Donald Coffey dies at 85." Johns Hopkins University. Accessed on November 11, 2019. https://hub.jhu.edu/2017/11/12/donald-coffey-obit/

"Paige: We are transforming the diagnosis and treatment of cancer." PAIGE. Accessed on March 31, 2020. https://paige.ai/

"Pathology Evolved: Advanced learning toward faster, more accurate diagnosis of disease." PathAI. Accessed on February 1, 2020. https://www.pathai.com/

"Pathology's Digital Future." Johns Hopkins Biomedical Engineering. Accessed on November 14, 2019. https://www.bme.jhu.edu/news-events/news/pathologys-digital-future/

CHAPTER 9: DRUG DISCOVERY AND DEVELOPMENT

"Artificial Intelligence in Health Care: Benefits and Challenges of Machine Learning in Drug Development." Government Accountability Office. December 2019.

Avorn, Jerry. "The $2.6 Billion Pill—Methodologic and Policy Considerations." *New England Journal of Medicine* 372, 20 (2015): 1877-1879.

BenevolentAI, "How we work." Accessed on October 15, 2019. https://benevolent.ai/how-we-work

Bowman, Greg. "Folding@Home Takes Up the Fight Against COVID-19/ 2019-NCOV." Folding@Home. Accessed on February 28, 2020. https://foldingathome.org/2020/02/27/folding-home-takes-up-the-fight-against-covid-19-2019-ncov/

Brown, Nathan, Marco Fiscato, Marwin Segler, and Alain Vaucher. "GuacaMol: Benchmarking Models for de Novo Molecular Design." *Journal of Chemical Information and Modeling* 59 (2019): 1096-1108.

Brown, William, Christopher Foote, Brent Iverson. *Organic Chemistry*. Belmont, CA.: Thomson Brooks/Cole, 2005.

Chikarmane, Roshan. "Business Innovation: A Cure for the Drug Pricing Dilemma." Biomedical Odyssey: Life at the Johns Hopkins School of Medicine. Accessed on March 15, 2020. https://biomedicalodyssey.blogs.hopkinsmedicine. org/2020/03/businesses-innovation-a-cure-for-the-drug-pricing-dilemma/

Egner, Patricia, Jian-Guo Chen, Adam Zarth, Derek Ng, Jin-Bing Wang, Kevin Kensler, Lisa Jacobson, Alvaro Muñoz, Jamie Johnson, John Groopman, Jed Fahey, Paul Talalay, Jian Zhu, Tao-Yang Chen, Geng-Sun Qian, Steven Carmella, Stephen Hecht, and Thomas Kensler. "Rapid and sustainable detoxication of airborne pollutants by broccoli sprout beverage: results of a randomized clinical trial in China." *Cancer Prevention Research* 7, no. 8 (2014): 813–823.

Egner, Patricia, Jian Guo Chen, Jin Wang, Yan Wu, Yan Sun, Jian Lu, Jian Zhu, Yong Zhang, Yong Chen, Marlin Friesen, Lisa Jacobson, Alvaro Muñoz, Derek Ng, Geng Qian, Yuan Zhu, Tao Chen, Nigel Botting, Qingzhi Zhang, Jed Fahey, Paul Talalay, John Groopman and Thomas Kensler. "Bioavailability of Sulforaphane from Two Broccoli Sprout Beverages: Results of a Short-term, Cross-over Clinical Trial in Qidong, China." *Cancer Prevention Research* 4, no. 3 (2011): 384-95.

Fauqueur, Julien, Ashok Thillaisundaram, and Theodosia Togia. "Constructing large scale biomedical knowledge bases from scratch with rapid annotation of interpretable patterns." Cornell University, last revised on July 3, 2019.

Fussell, Chris. *One Mission: How Leaders Build a Team of Teams.* New York: Portfolio/Penguin, 2017.

Kensler, Thomas, Derek Ng, Steven Carmella, Menglan Chen, Lisa Jacobson, Álvaro Muñoz, Patricia Egner, Jian-Guo Chen, Geng Qian, Tao Chen, Jed Fahey, Paul Talalay, John Groopman, Jian-Min Yuan, Stephen Hecht. "Modulation of the metabolism of airborne pollutants by glucoraphanin-rich and sulforaphane-rich broccoli sprout beverages in Qidong, China." *Carcinogenesis.* 33, no. 1 (2011): 101-107.

Narasimhan, Vas, Jorge Conde, Vijay Pande, and Sonal Chokshi. "Science, Business, and Innovation in Big Pharma: A Conversation with Novartis' CEO." Andreessen Horowitz.

NVIDIA. "Nvidia and BenevolentAI—Accelerating Scientific Discovery with AI." December 21, 2016. Video, 2:50. https://youtu.be/qtkZt5u1XE8

Paul, Steven, Daniel Mytelka, Christopher Dunwiddie, Charles Persinger, Bernard Munos, Stacy Lindborg, Aaron Schacht. "How to improve R&D productivity: the pharmaceutical industry's grand challenge." *Nature Reviews Drug Discovery 9* (2010): 203–214.

SETI@home. "The science of SETI@home." University of California at Berkeley. Accessed on February 20, 2020. https://setiathome.berkeley.edu/sah_about.php

Ward, Andrew. "Big pharma seeks digital solution to productivity problem." Financial Times. April 1, 2016.

Warner, Christina. "The Future of Healthcare With Brad Bostic, CEO of hc1." Thrive Global. Accessed on December 18, 2019. https://thriveglobal.com/stories/the-future-of-healthcare-with-brad-bostic-ceo-of-hc1/

Zhavoronkov, Alex, Yan Ivanenkov, Alex Aliper, Mark Veselov, Vladimir Aladinskiy, Anastasiya Aladinskaya, Victor Terentiev, Daniil Polykovskiy, Maksim Kuznetsov, Arip Asadulaev, Yury Volkov, Artem Zholus, Rim Shayakhmetov, Alexander Zhebrak, Lidiya Minaeva, Bogdan Zagribelnyy, Lennart Lee, Richard Soll, David Madge, Li Xing, Tao Guo, and Alán Aspuru-Guzik. "Deep Learning enables rapid identification of potent DDR1 kinase inhibitors." *Nature Biotechnology* 37 (2019): 1038–1040.

CHAPTER 10: MEDICAL ADMINISTRATION AND AI

Auerbach, Andrew, Sunil Kripalani, Eduard Vasilevskis, Neil Sehgal, Peter Lindenauer, Joshua Metlay, Grant Fletcher, Gregory Ruhnke, Scott Flanders, Christopher Kim, Mark Williams, Larissa Thomas, Vernon Giang, Shoshana Herzig, Kanan Patel, John Boscardin, Edmondo Robinson, Jeffrey Schnipper. "Preventability and causes of readmissions in a national cohort of general medicine patients." *JAMA Internal Medicine* 176, no. 4 (2016): 484-493.

AngelList Weekly, email message to author, October 17, 2019.

Go Sibyl. Accessed on January 17, 2020. https://www.gosibyl.com/

Hospital Readmissions Reduction Program (HRRP). Centers for Medicare and Medicaid Services. Accessed on January 11, 2020. https://www.cms.gov/Medicare/Medicare-Fee-for-Service-Payment/AcuteInpatientPPS/Readmissions-Reduction-Program

Japsen, Bruce. "Doctor Wait Times Soar 30% in Major US Cities." Forbes. Accessed on November 2, 2019. https://www.forbes.com/sites/brucejapsen/2017/03/19/doctor-wait-times-soar-amid-trumpcare-debate/#58b848e2e740

Jencks, Stephen, Mark Williams, and Eric Coleman. "Rehospitalizations among patients in the Medicare fee-for-service program," *New England Journal of Medicine* 360, no. 14(2009): 1418-1428.

Johnson, Gregory. "The Cost of a US Hospital Readmission." Accessed on October 20, 2019. https://www.slideshare.net/GregoryJohnson10/the-cost-of-a-us-hospital-readmission

Medicare Payment Advisory Commission. *Report to the Congress: Promoting Greater Efficiency in Medicare.* Washington, DC: Medicare Payment Advisory Commission; 2007.

Merkow, Ryan, Mila Ju, Jeanette Chung, Bruce Hall, Mark Cohen, Mark Williams, Thomas Tsai, Clifford Ko, and Karl Bilimoria. "Underlying Reasons Associated with Hospital

Readmission Following Surgery in the United States." *JAMA*. 313, no. 5 (2015): 483-95.

Morgan, Daniel, Bill Bame, Paul Zimand, Patrick Dooley, Kerri Thorn, Anthony Harris, Soren Bentzen, Walt Ettinger, Stacy Garrett-Ray, J. Kathleen Tract, and Yuanyuan Liang. "Assessment of Machine Learning vs Standard Prediction Rules for Predicting Hospital Readmissions." *JAMA Network Open*. 2, no. 3 (2019).

Report for Selected Countries and Subjects. International Monetary Fund. Accessed on September 20, 2019. https://www.imf. org/external/pubs/ft/weo/2019/02/weodata/weorept.aspx?pr. x=79&pr.y=12&sy=2016&ey=2021&scsm=1&ssd=1&sort=country&ds=.&br=1&c=111&s=NGDP_RPCH%2CNGDP-D%2CPPPGDP%2CNGDPDPC%2CPPPPC%2CPCPIP-CH&grp=0&a

Schneider, Eric, Dana Sarnak, David Squires, Arnav Shah, and Michelle Doty.

"Mirror, Mirror 2017: International Comparison Reflects Flaws and Opportunities for Better US Health Care." The Commonwealth Fund. Accessed on September 28, 2019. https://www.commonwealthfund.org/publications/fund-reports/2017/jul/mirror-mirror-2017-international-comparison-reflects-flaws-and

Shrank, William, Teresa Rogstad, and Natasha Parekh. "Waste in the US Health Care System Estimated Costs and Potential for Savings." *JAMA* 322, no. 15 (2019).

"The world's most powerful data lives on Quandl." Quandl. Accessed on September 1, 2019. https://www.quandl.com/

Tseng, Phillip, Robert Kaplan, Barak Richman, Mahek Shah, and Kevin Schulman. "Administrative Costs Associated with Physician Billing and Insurance-Related Activities at an Academic Health Care System." *JAMA* 319, no. 7 (2018): 691-697.

Xu, Keyang, Mike Lam, Jingzhi Pang, Xin Gao, Charlotte Band, Piyush Mathur, Frank Papay, Ashish Khanna, Jacek Cywinski, Kamal Maheshwari, Pengtao Xie, Eric Xing. "Multimodal Machine Learning for Automated ICD Coding." *Proceedings of Machine Learning Research* 106 (2019): 1–17.

Zuckerman, Rachael, Steven Sheingold, E. John Orav, Joel Ruhter, and Arnold Epstein. "Readmissions, Observation, and the Hospital Readmissions Reduction Program." *New England Journal of Medicine* 374 (2016): 1543-1551.

CHAPTER 11: A CULTURE OF CREATION

Bourke, Daniel. "My Self-Created Artificial Intelligence Masters Degree." Accessed on September 19, 2019. https://www.mrdbourke.com/aimastersdegree/

"Engineering next-generation, brain-penetrant cancer therapies." Reverie Labs. Accessed on September 29, 2019. https://www.reverielabs.com/

Fast Grants. "Fast Funding for COVID-19 Science." Accessed May 1, 2020. https://fastgrants.org/

Johns Hopkins University Hub. "Online map tracks drive-through COVID-19 testing sites across the U.S." Accessed May 1, 2020. https://hub.jhu.edu/2020/04/29/drive-through-coronavirus-testing-map-jim-kyung-soo-liew/

Kaufman, Rachel. "Sewage May Hold the Key to Tracking Opioid Abuse." Smithsonian Magazine. August 22, 2018.

"Making the Leap to Precision Medicine." Bullfrog AI: Precision Pharma. Accessed on January 8, 2020. https://www.bullfrogai.com/

"Research for the People." National Institutes of Health. US Department of Health and Human Services. Accessed on February 20, 2020. https://www.nih.gov/about-nih/what-we-do/budget

"What Happens at Y Combinator." Y Combinator. Accessed on September 2, 2019. https://www.ycombinator.com/atyc/

Y Combinator. Accessed on July 11, 2019. https://www.ycombinator.com/

"YC Companies: Artificial Intelligence." Y Combinator. Accessed on July 11, 2019. https://www.ycombinator.com/companies/?vertical=Artificial%20Intelligence

"YC Companies: Health care." Y Combinator. Accessed on July 11, 2019. https://www.ycombinator.com/companies/?vertical=Healthcare

CHAPTER 12: CONCLUSION

Cohen, I. Glenn. "Ethics & the Law – I. Glenn Cohen, Professor of Law at Harvard University – Technology, Law, Ethics, and What's on the Horizon." August 20, 2019. In *Finding Genius Podcast Future Tech Edition*. Produced by Richard Jacobs. Podcast, 35:44. https://futuretech.findinggeniuspodcast.com/podcasts/ethics-the-law-i-glenn-cohen-professor-of-law-at-harvard-university-technology-law-ethics-and-whats-on-the-horizon/

"Customers." Montuno Software. Accessed on November 5, 2019. https://www.montunosoftware.com/customers/

Harvard Global Health Institute. "I. Glenn Cohen—AI in Healthcare: Legal and Ethical Issues." May 23, 2019. Video, 11:06. https://youtu.be/oRuL6kzg7wo

Jordan, Michael I. "Artificial Intelligence—The revolution hasn't happened yet." Amazon Science. Accessed on November 25, 2019. https://www.amazon.science/artificial-intelligence-the-revolution-hasnt-happened-yet

Sherer, Lori. "Yoky Matsuoka of Google Health on the Future of Health care." Bain and Company. Accessed on July 6, 2019. https://www.bain.com/insights/yoky-matsuoka-of-google-health-on-the-future-of-healthcare/

Made in the USA
Middletown, DE
30 July 2020